ANY ADVANCE?

We are all fascinated by the secret language and customs of trades and professions. Through the adventures and misadventures of Willy Shaun, Geoffrey Johns introduces us to the world of auctions and antique dealers. It is a world where quickness of wit is a necessity and knowledge of human nature is essential.

This is a novel for members of the trade, whose secrets Geoffrey Johns has deftly brought to light, for the private collector who wants to know what to look for in a William and Mary bow-fronted chest-of-drawers, and the merely curious. *Any Advance?* is a humorous and fascinating novel that takes the lid off a world few of us know. Auctions can never be the same again.

To Paulette

with compliments

Geoffrey Hosking

GEOFFREY JOHNS

ANY ADVANCE?

Illustrated by

DEREK WILLIAMS

HUTCHINSON OF LONDON

HUTCHINSON & CO. (*Publishers*) LTD
178–202 Great Portland Street, London, W.1

London Melbourne Sydney
Auckland Bombay Toronto
Johannesburg New York

First published 1961

*This book has been set in Fournier type face. It has
been printed in Great Britain by The Anchor Press,
Ltd., in Tiptree, Essex, on Antique Wove paper
and bound by Taylor Garnett Evans & Co., Ltd., in
Watford, Herts*

Contents

Contents

Foreword

Like the characters, the incidents in this book are fictitious, though founded on fact. A genuine description is given of all the antiques with the exception of the 'Chinese Chippendale pagoda cabinet'; this, for reasons of discretion, is invented.

The 'Ring', like most institutions that have grown up by custom, varies according to local usage and the exigencies of the moment; its workings, too, can be extremely complicated. But the incidents described here in a simplified form are typical of what goes on in salerooms up and down the country.

Under Lord Chief Justice Darling's Act, the Auctions (Bidding Agreements) Act 1927, the whole affair is an illegal conspiracy, but owing to the difficulties of proof there has never been a successful prosecution.

The 'Ring', the 'Knockout', and the 'Settlement' are terms which are used interchangeably in the trade, but their original meanings are as follows: the 'Ring' refers to the conspiracy not to bid; the 'Knockout' is the re-auction that takes place privately among dealers after a sale and establishes the final owner; the 'Settlement' is the dividing up of the difference between the price originally paid under the hammer and the much bigger one finally paid.

1 The Bottom of the Ladder

William Shaun was born and bred in the back streets of Torminster, a large West Country town, in a quarter where it was not safe for a stranger to walk alone at night. He was an only child, but in this kind of district no child, not even an only one, was ever spoilt. They all had to learn the hard way. He was a proper Willy; black-haired, sharp-eyed—always the first to put his foot on a dropped halfpenny. Time and time again he experienced the sharp gripes of hunger pinching his little tummy, as his pinched-in cheeks and small bony frame showed. His mother had passed into another world—a happier one no doubt—by the time Willy had reached the age of four. In his later life he had to think hard to remember what she was like.

His father possessed a rag-and-bone business. The junk was offered for sale in the two small front rooms facing on to the street, while the rag-and-bone side of it was consigned to the large yard at the rear of the premises. Willy received very little schooling, whether or not he went depending on what Shaun senior was doing on any particular day.

The end of the 1914–18 war found Torminster prospering and ready to expand. The thirteenth-century Abbey, with its two squat towers, looked across the River Tor to the old corn mills whose stone walls had stood for three centuries or more. Acres of what had once been water-meadows had been encroached upon to house the gradual increase in the working population. In the centre of the town the broad, steep

High Street, with its bow-fronted shop-windows and tall Corn Exchange, would soon see the first of the chain stores. From there the streets ran out winding and narrow; at first of antiquarian interest, a Mecca for tourists, then, towards the east at least, through a hotch-potch of mid-Victorian back-to-backs, the odd persisting mediaeval cob-and-thatch, small one-man factories and engineering works, petering out in dead-end streets, or vacant lots (whose value was soon to be exploited), or being stopped short by the railway lines. East Street, where Mr Shaun carried on his business, came out near the junction of the main lines and the shunting yards, and when he was free—which wasn't often—Willy could play leap-frog with the other boys over the iron rails, their boots clattering on the cold metal; or he could watch the trucks being shunted past, or gaze up at the eastern sky towards nightfall, cold over the gas-works and the railway yards; or if he walked a little way there was a hump-backed iron bridge over a tributary stream, once a shallow reedy trout-stream, now rust-coloured from a dye-works, from which you could see a bend of the river and the dark hulk of the Abbey. But Willy was never one for leaning or lazing or staring into the middle distance: he had an eye for the main chance, and life lay right under his nose.

Shaun's business was next door to a coach-repairer's and Willy sometimes made himself useful there and earned a copper or two. He also learnt how to handle woodworking tools. These few coppers were a source of great satisfaction and pride, as his father never gave him any pocket-money.

The arrival of a motor-car in the coach-yard was the biggest moment East Street had experienced. The car was in need of body repairs, and was the first of a trickle which turned into a stream, changing the nature of the business, and eventually the outlook of the whole street. The coach-repairing yard quickly became a motor-repairing garage with a growing reputation and a growing appetite for expansion. Down came the block of flea-ridden tenements next to Shaun's and up went show-rooms and offices.

The business of Shaun senior had also undergone a change. During the war the rag-and-bone side of it had laid a solid foundation, and now, after the war, it took second place in response to something which had begun to be fashionable—the craze for collecting antiques and curios. This all sounds very grand; but what it amounted to was the clearance from the yard of evil-smelling rags and worse-smelling bones, and the erection of three corrugated-iron-roofed open lean-to's right round the yard. The two front shop-windows were enlarged and the two front rooms made into one large showroom. The quality of the junk offered for sale was somewhat better and the business now possessed a pony-and-trap. Gone for ever was the handcart. Kruger, as the pony was called, had his stabling in the lean-to on the far side of the yard. He was well fed, indifferently groomed, and had to work mighty hard for his living.

Shaun senior knew nothing about antiques whatsoever. Neither did his son. The father was a hard worker, scavenging the countryside, sales, jumble sales, rubbish tips—wherever odds and ends of this and that might be going cheap or perhaps even being given away. You could tell how hard he worked by the sheer amount of stuff piled in the shop and out in the yard.

In 1923 Willy officially left school, some of the three R's having been fixed in his head mostly by cuff and cane. His father exacted a hard week's work and he was allowed two shillings spending money at the end of it.

When he was fifteen years old an incident occurred which could be called the starting point of his career. He was out in one of the back rooms, rubbing his fingers nearly to the bone in an unsuccessful effort to remove the verdigris from a pair of brass candlesticks. His father was in the front shop trying to sell something to two women wanting a wedding present.

'There now,' said old Shaun, pointing to a large oval glass bowl, 'there's a good bit o' glass. Cut-glass it is, for sure. Do you very nicely for the wedding present. 'S in perfect condition.' The bowl was taken down from the shelf and carefully examined.

'How much?' enquired the elder of the two women.

'Six bob, an' cheap at that.'

'Oh!—far too much for a piece of second-hand glass. Not worth more than three shillings, and anyway we told you we didn't want to spend much more than two-and-six.'

'Yer can 'ave it for five bob an' I'll not take less,' was the surly retort. He had got the bowl in a lot of humble-jumble bought at a small village sale for seven shillings and sixpence. He had no intention of fooling it away, however. He knew it was cut-glass and worth the five bob he was asking for it.

At that moment Joseph Steen walked into the shop. He was a London dealer specializing in antique porcelain and glass and knew a good thing when he saw it. He often came West on his buying trips and no shop in the country was too small or too dirty for him to poke his big nose inside for bargains.

He waited a few moments listening to Shaun senior selling the bowl, then slipped into the back room where he could hear Willy working on the brass.

'Here, boy,' he whispered sharply. 'Do you know what your old man's doing out there? He's trying to sell an eighteenth-century Irish glass bowl to a couple of women for five bob and it's worth every penny of twenty quid. For Pete's sake go out there and stop him!'

Willy acted promptly and with great cunning. Going to the door he called out: 'Just a minute, Dad. I've got to speak to you. Mr Steen wants to know the price of something. He can't stop as he has a train to catch.'

''Scuse me,' said old Shaun to his customers. 'Shan't be a second.'

In a moment or two he was back.

'Sorry for the interruption. Now, missus, if you're giving the thing as a present I'd better clean some of this dirt out of the inside. You can wash it when it's home but I'll get the worst out. Haven't even had a chance to wash it—only brought it back yesterday.' So saying, he picked up the glass bowl and disappeared.

Out in the back room, after a suitable pause, Willy picked up three chipped glass pint mugs and with a noise sufficient to wake the dead sent them crashing on the brick floor. Back out into the shop went old Shaun with a well-simulated look of sorrow and disgust on his face.

'Been an' dropped the bloomin' thing,' he blurted out. 'Smashed to bits. Proper gonner. Better 'ave your five bob back, I suppose.'

The two ladies expressed their sorrow and annoyance and went to look elsewhere.

Back in the shop Shaun *v*. Steen were having a heated argument.

'I'm not giving you anything like twenty quid—dammit, you were selling it for five bob! You can keep it till the cows come home and you wouldn't get that price here in this shop. Five pounds is what I'm giving you and you don't deserve even that.'

The bowl eventually changed hands for six pounds, Steen secretly slipping Willy a ten-shilling note for the part he had played.

Old Steen is a proper toff, thought Willy as he fingered his first-ever ten-shilling note. This is real money.

Later that evening Willy related the episode to his pal Ginger who was helping him spend some of the ten shillings. Naturally he greatly exaggerated the part he had played.

'The trouble with Dad is that he just doesn't know. One thing is the same as another to him.'

Willy had been wondering all the afternoon, since Steen's departure, just how many lots his father had sold for shillings which might have been worth as many or more pounds. He came to the conclusion that if he was to succeed in life and be like Joseph Steen he must get hold of knowledge.

From then onwards he hung about outside the shops of other antique dealers; peering in through the windows, always questioning the sale-room porters, who, he soon found out, knew very little more than he did. He made himself a real nuisance at the local museum whenever he got the chance to go. To get rid of him one day the assistant curator lent him a book on pottery and porcelain. A huge book it was, by a man called Chaffers—an old edition. Willy was asked to sign for it and told not to bring it back until he had learnt everything in it off by heart. This treasure opened up a new world for him; he studied it for hours into the night or until his candle gave out. Some of the words were unintelligible, but he got a general idea of the different products of the various factories, whose marks he was able to remember with a remarkable accuracy.

Soon he was able to use what he learnt.

One day old Shaun brought home a vast load of odds and ends in which were two cups and saucers. They were of simple design, rather rough in the body, and the only decoration was floral swagging round the border of both cup and saucer, executed in a dirty-looking green. On the bottom of each cup was a blue cross and the numeral 6. The saucers were unmarked. Willy had an idea about these and took a quick look in his book upstairs.

'No doubt about it. Bristol. That's what they are.'

In the meantime old man Shaun was sorting his various acquisitions out and marking them off. After a bit Willy casually began to ask what some of the prices were, including the two cups and saucers.

'Not very good decoration on these, Dad. What do they stand in at?'

'Oh, them! About fourpence each. Oughter sell all right. Cups and saucers always sell. Get about eightpence each and I should think they might have a bit of age about them.'

'Take sixpence each for them if we've got to, I suppose?' said his son.

'Aye. Take a profit on them, lad. If you always take a profit you'll do all right.'

Willy put the cups and saucers up on a shelf, tucking them well out of sight behind something else. That afternoon, when his father was out again, he wrapped them up and hid them in his bedroom. Four shillings still remained from Joseph Steen's generosity, so he put two shillings in the small biscuit-tin they used as a cash register and took out sixpence change, proudly announcing to his father later on that he had sold the cups and saucers for one-and-six—more than they had expected to get.

'Who bought them?'

'I dunno, Dad—never seen the bloke before. Had to fight hard to get the price.'

Later in the week he had to do a delivery, and used the opportunity to take the cups and saucers round to Benson, who had an antique shop in the classy part of the town.

'These any good to you, Mr. Benson?'

Old Mr Benson examined the cups and saucers carefully.

'Could be, boy, could be. How much do you want for them?'

This floored Willy. He was certain they were Bristol porcelain but had no idea of their market value.

'Three quid,' he said, hopefully.

'Does your father really expect to get three pounds for these?' countered Benson, who was wise in the ways of dealing. Willy felt uncomfortable, so came straight to the point.

'They aren't his. They're mine. I haven't nicked them—paid out my own cash for them. I think they're Bristol.'

'So, so,' mused the other-side-of-seventy Benson. He was rather surprised at young Shaun showing so much knowledge. He liked the kid, always so alert and eager.

'What makes you so certain that they are Bristol?'

'Been studying a book Mr. Tanner up at the Museum lent me.'

'Him! That's one way of finding out, but you will never learn all that much from a book. You've got to see and feel the stuff to know something about it. Your cups and saucers are not worth three pounds to me, boy, but I can give you thirty shillings. You are quite right about them being Bristol porcelain, but the quality is poor.'

Willy jumped at the offer. He had a lot yet to learn about dealing. Even in those days the pair were worth four pounds ten.

'Please don't mention our deal to the old man,' said Willy, pocketing the largest amount of money he had ever possessed. 'He'll only take it off me.'

'No. I will not mention it, boy. You can bring me any other thing you think may interest me, providing you have come by it honestly.'

Benson chuckled as Willy left the shop. Well pleased with his side of the bargain, he had also added another 'runner' to his list, a sharp runner at that, albeit a young one.

Willy left Benson's shop with the idea firmly fixed in his mind that he was on the way up. One day he too would have a shop like that and deal with all the Toffs. Why, old Benson had things in his shop worth fifty pounds each.

Homeward bound after delivering his parcel, he passed Sedge's second-hand bookshop. After his success in the 'china' world, 'glass' was going to be his next conquest. He could see no books on the subject of antique glass in the penny bargain troughs outside, so in he went.

''Afternoon, Mr Sedge. Mind if I look round?'

Sedge raised his eyebrows in astonishment. This was the first time he had ever known that young back-street urchin Shaun to show any interest in books. Often he had seen both the young one and his father scavenging for odd lots of rubbish in the sale-rooms. Probably thinks he can pinch a book or two when I'm not looking, thought the suspicious Sedge.

'What d'you want, young' un? I don't let just any Tom, Dick, or Harry look round in here.'

'I want a book on antique glass—Irish glass.' If Joseph Steen could reckon that glass bowl to be Irish and worth twenty quid, the money was obviously in Irish glass.

Meanwhile Sedge produced a rather tatty-covered book dealing with both Irish and English glass. It was an instructive volume, even though nearly all the illustrations were of pieces in the possession of the principal museums and private collections. The finest of their type, no doubt, but unlikely ever again to come the way of either dealer or collector. A good many books on antiques bolt down the same hole when it comes to illustrations.

'How much?'

'Four-an'-six. It cost a guinea new.'

'By the look of this cover that must have been a long time ago. I've only got half a crown.'

Sedge hesitated. He had not sold very much that day and the book had only cost him eightpence.

'All right. The book's yours. Let's see the money.'

Willy put the book under his arm and produced the ten-shilling note, realizing as he did so that he had boobed.

'Thought you said you only had half a crown?' accused Sedge with a sharp edge of sarcasm.

'Not buyin' it for myself,' lied the purchaser with brazen impudence; 'the ten bob don't belong to me.'

'Where the 'ell 'ave you bin?' enquired the elder Shaun when his son returned. 'You' bin talking to any girls?' This was a growing bone of contention between them, for Willy had just reached the age to take interest in the opposite sex. The only apparent difference it made to him was that he now plastered a lot of evil-perfumed grease on his hair which he parted meticulously in the middle.

'Got hung up with the parcel. No one in, and the person next door said to wait as they wouldn't be gone long. Ain't seen a girl worth talking to all the way.'

Two years passed and the East Street business was prospering as it had never done before. Shaun had already perceived that his son had what he called 'a flair' for the business.

'Buy quality, Dad, buy quality,' Willy was for ever saying. He allowed Willy five shillings a week, recognizing at long last that he was entitled to a few decent clothes and a drink or two with the lads of his own age.

Willy had also prospered—to an extent which would have shaken his father had the latter known it. Dozens of quite valuable antiques had passed through Willy's hands, most of them coming from the shop.

In his favour it must be said that he always paid into the biscuit-tin the amount his father expected to get; very occasionally, when his conscience pricked him, he even paid in more. In these two years he had accumulated the sum of seventy-eight pounds. His library now included a book on silver, three on English furniture, and two books on oil paintings. These, as yet, he knew nothing about, and had not ventured to put any of his money into paintings.

Some of his lots were still being sold to Mr. Benson, but after having seen a good many of them reappear in Benson's window at a later date, marked up at a price about four times what Benson had paid him for them, he got artful and began using his evening street-corner pals to further his own business. It was so simple. When he got hold of something he knew would interest Benson he 'planted' it in the house of one of his friends, whose mother would promptly call on Benson with the story that they had an antique at home which a certain young man by the name of Shaun was repeatedly trying to buy from them. They didn't trust him all that much. In the first place he was rather young (this always got the better of Benson), and secondly he refused to make any offer but insisted that they should tell him what they were prepared to take for it. They didn't know how much it was worth and anyway it was preferable to do business with a reputable firm.

It wasn't long before Benson was there on the doorstep, knowing that if he wanted the object he would have to bid, and bid a good price, to put it beyond the reach of William S., or make that young man burn his fingers.

When he had, some child or other was invariably sent off to get 'father's' final agreement. If they didn't find Willy at the shop old Benson had to wait a day for his answer. This always made him very cross, his suspicions being that the thing would be 'hawked around' to other dealers to find out if a better price could be got.

Naturally Willy had to pay small commissions, but he did much better this way. He never used the same house or story twice to the same dealer. His back-street friends were numerous and widely scattered round the town.

The ominous rumblings of the coming slump left the Shauns unperturbed. They followed their code that if a man is prepared to work hard he will never starve. The General Strike came and went; they saw near-starvation around them. Strong men, neighbours, purposefully idle, gradually drawing in their belts.

'Lot of bloody fools, that's what they are,' was the remark always on the old man's lips.

Business gradually deteriorated, so they worked the harder, here, there, anywhere a shilling could be made, father and son drawn closer to each other in adversity than they had ever been before. Shaun senior was getting on a bit, for he had been fifty years old when Willy was born.

Despite the hard times Willy was courting: his fancy was a waitress over at the Star Hotel, in a better part of the town. She was a smart little baggage with a fat round bottom and all sorts of ideas about class. She considered Willy Shaun quite a lot beneath her dignity and would have nothing to do with anyone who lived in East Street. One day she accidentally saw him pull out a wad of notes—more than a dozen of her other boy friends possessed between them. There was well over two hundred pounds in that roll and he was only twenty years old.

From then onwards she began to take notice of William Shaun. It was not just the money—she understood how he'd come by it. She saw the restless vitality within the frame of a still thinnish body—a vitality as restless as the wide-set black eyes beneath a shock of black hair with a curl that was always tickling his eyebrow. Good-looking? Hardly, but she wanted a husband not a film star and she realized she stood the chance of backing a winner.

Ethel Field was Shaun's complementary opposite. Fair-haired, roundish-faced, and buxom, she was considered good-looking and was much sought after; she took a teasing delight in making Willy jealous.

The rows between them were often fast and furious, but they were married in 1931. They moved in above the shop and the old man took a room over the road.

The 'Ring', an illegal arrangement by which dealers agree not to bid against one another at an auction sale and are thus able to buy an article for much less than it is worth, was by now well established amongst the antique traders of Torminster.

The old man Shaun did not go in for it. It was all miles above his head and anyway he now preferred nosing around the countryside away from Torminster with Kruger the pony, and the trap.

Willy, on the other hand, was in the thick of it. At first some of the dealers refused to acknowledge him as one of themselves, but Willy succeeded in making himself such a nuisance in the sale-rooms, by bidding on and raising the price of every lot which came up, that they were eventually glad to let him into the ring.

Benson was responsible for most of his success. Benson himself did not belong to the ring and seldom went to a sale if he could avoid it. His business was too well established and his private clientele too valuable for him to want to associate himself with something which was considered 'not nice'.

However, he was always pleased to buy from Willy any lot in which he could see a profit, and didn't think it his business to ask how he had come by it. He taught Willy a lot about values and also took a few of his things 'on sale or return', provided Willy had not bought them at a sale in the near neighbourhood. These were the lots Willy got 'landed with' in the private illegal re-auction through being too greedy. They stood a better chance of being sold from Benson's shop than they would have done from East Street. Willy, through his own financial losses, which hurt considerably, and the knowledgeable old man's tuition, gradually came to be quite a good judge of antiques in general. He had long since given up his mean little tricks on Benson, but continued them as before with others.

Ethel was quite a good needlewoman. Times without number she carefully unpicked the date from Victorian samplers, bought for a shilling or so. To add an eighteenth-century date was easy, sometimes the alteration of an eight into a seven sufficing. She used the same thread she had unpicked and when she had carefully brushed a little cold tea over the new work, toning it down to match the rest, it was practically impossible to detect the alteration. These faked samplers were then put back in various sale-rooms to be purchased by private punters, sometimes even by the antique dealers, for as many pounds as they had cost shillings.

Singeing the edges of modern reproduction prints in front of the fire was another good dodge. These prints, 'Shooting', 'Hunting', 'Cock-fighting', 'Bull-baiting', all good selling subjects, could be bought from Solomon Levert for about one shilling each. He came round regularly with a large folio of them, and how he ever made a living at it Willy was at a loss to know. The idea was to make all the borders nice and brown, simulating age, but not to spoil the actual print. The method of dipping the whole print in coffee had long since been exposed, and was far too obvious on close examination.

The singeing idea was much more subtle; the only way to tell if it was fake or genuine was to get the print out of the frame and look at the actual paper on which it was printed. The frames came along two-a-penny, were always chosen with care, and, if possible, the dirty old piece of backing paper was carefully steamed off and replaced after the faked print was behind the glass, which was, of course, not cleaned on the inside. As most sale-room porters were loth to allow prints to be taken out of their frames, this was a very remunerative line for Willy.

In 1937 Ethel and Willy had a daughter, christened Ann. Much to Willy's surprise, his father paid half the expenses—things had not been straightforward and private nursing-home arrangements had had to be made. Old Mr Shaun was more or less retired now, having handed over the shop to Willy some time back, but was quite content to sit in it and sell any of his son's goods.

Willy often wondered about his father. The old 'un never seemed short of a penny or two and often picked up the odd bit of silver here and there, silver which he never seemed to sell. The business now sported a van, purchased from the garage next door, second-hand, but a good bargain. One of the corrugated lean-to's had been taken down and remade into a properly covered garage, and poor old Kruger and the trap had been sold. As Willy had explained to his father, you can't afford to mix sentiment with business, but the old man cried when the pony went. They had been good friends together.

The rumblings were getting louder and louder in Europe. Shaun senior often shook his head. 'Coming, lad—it's coming! Blast them stupid politicians! Aye, Labour Party an' all. If it hadn't been for them and their policy of disarm, disarm, we wouldn't be in trouble now.'

Willy was far too busy making a living to worry about what was going on in Germany. That country was a long way away and he had three mouths to feed now instead of two.

The war came and caught him completely unprepared. He had read the papers and things seemed to be very sticky, the whole international situation looked black, but, he supposed, newspapermen had to make the worst of everything in order to sell their rags.

He was called up shortly after war broke out, just about the time his father got himself run over in the blackout—army lorry—didn't stop. He had left everything to his son—the shop property, one hundred and eighty pounds in the bank, and all his personal effects. And what a surprise Willy got when he went through the two attic bedrooms that the old man had kept on over the shop! No one was ever allowed up there. The door at the bottom of the attic staircase was always kept locked, as Ethel knew, since with the usual feminine curiosity she had tried that door many times.

'Can't think what he keeps up there,' she used to say to Willy. 'Place must be like a pigsty—never hear him tidying up.'

Willy made a methodical search, turning out every drawer in an old oak chest of drawers not worth five bob. All they seemed to contain was bills and old papers. But in the bottom drawer, amongst more papers, was a round flat decorated biscuit-tin. It seemed to weigh a ton as it was lifted out. Inside were exactly two hundred gold sovereigns—a souvenir of the rag-and-bone business of the 1914–18 war. All through the depression which had followed this little nest-egg had remained untouched.

Willy quickly calculated the current market value of those sovereigns as he sorted through some baskets, finding nothing of value but a decent gold back-collar-stud. All the contents had obviously belonged to his mother, and he was a little sad as he turned them over. Try as he might the only picture of his mother he could conjure up was a vague face, looking at him with loving eyes, but all these memories seemed so far away and hazy. He hoped perhaps to find a photograph, but there wasn't one. In the other room, no more than a large cupboard with a skylight, he found five bulging sacks and two large boxes. Silver—silver—and more silver! Willy whistled. He soon saw that the stuff was of no outstanding quality, but nearly every piece was worth more than scrap price. Most of it was of the Edwardian and late Victorian periods, but here and there he came on a Georgian piece. He went downstairs for his silver scales. Over eight thousand ounces was his rough approximation. Whew! Ikey and Moses! he thought, where did he get all this from?—must have been hoarding it for years! No wonder there was only one hundred and eighty pounds in the bank—thought he should have had more than that. Jumping crackers!—what's to be done with this lot?

As soon as he asked himself that question the answer came, born of inherent instincts: Get it out of the way of any snooping probate official who might see fit to have a good search round the house. Wait, better be careful. Do a bit of sorting out and leave one of the boxes here in the house. Perhaps have to pay some death duties on the contents, but then it would be on record that Terrence Shaun left some silver to his son. Everything had to be done in a hurry: only ten days were left to settle all his own private affairs as well as everything else.

The silver disappeared out of the house at top speed, safely lodged with Ethel's parents in five tea-chests with lids well nailed down and sealed with sealing-wax. The deeds of the property were obtained from the bank and from then onwards a small local firm of solicitors handled everything.

The tin of gold sovereigns was given to Ethel for safe keeping, on the understanding that if anything happened to Willy she was to use her own discretion about selling them, but not to part with them more than one at a time and no more than five or six to any one particular jeweller or dealer.

Even during the hubbub and bustle of his approaching departure for the Army, Willy had a few moments for reflection: The old 'un knew a thing or two. Couldn't have had his money in anything better at a time

like this. The whole lot immediately transportable! Cunning old bastard
—wish I had his foresight!

Eventually the premises and contents of the house were appraised by
a local licensed valuer. Probate was granted and death duties settled. By
this time Willy was well and truly in the Army.

2 *Landed*

'You're in the Army now! You're in the Army now!'

Willy was fed up with that song already. He had reported at the
intake depot, passed his medical—classified A1—then Pay Book, Part
I and Part II, clothing, boots, equipment, respirator, rifle—the conveyor
belt carried him smoothly along to his interview with a drafting officer,
during which it was noted that he could drive a motor vehicle. He was
promptly sent to a special training centre and after the usual eight
weeks' preliminary training was posted as a driver to a supply depot.
This fitted in well with his idea of things; in this sort of work there was
always the chance of being able to pick up a shilling or two here and
there.

Six years later he left the Army as he had entered it—as a private; he
had seen service in France with the B.E.F., been machine-gunned in-
cessantly from the air while waiting on the beaches of Dunkirk, and
copped a bullet wound through the chest that kept him in England till
after D-Day. During this time he made the most of opportunities as they
presented themselves.

Every commodity was in short supply and the amount of 'fiddling' going on was almost unbelievable except to those who had access to the stuff or access to the statistics dealing with the loss of it. Tea, butter, sugar, petrol, clothing, almost anything was 'fiddled', even toilet paper—and not only in the Forces. How many civilians refused the offer of a bit more than their rations? The judge who sent down the odd offender against the rationing laws for six months wasn't likely to enquire how his wife was able to place an egg-and-bacon breakfast in front of him nearly every day.

Stealing in the Army was on the whole carefully organized. Woe betide anyone who stepped out of his allocation on to someone else's toes! He was posted to another unit in double-quick time.

At first Willy couldn't bring himself to go in for this kind of racketeering: keen business and sharp practice were one thing but downright theft was another, especially at a time when the country was down on her uppers.

One day he bumped into his old street-corner pal Ginger. Ginger had successfully dodged the column—was working as a concrete-mixing-machine-minder employed by a contractor making a fortune from Government contracts on the iniquitous scheme of costs-plus-profit. Ginger was working long hours, but admitted that he and his mates slowed down deliberately during normal hours so that overtime would have to be worked. After hearing that Ginger made fifteen to eighteen pounds a week Willy had no qualms about taking stuff which did not belong to him. Blankets were his speciality; once he had the luck to get away with five bundles of them—twenty to a bundle. There was no difficulty: a slight detour in his lorry took him to the back yard of a public house where he got spot cash, ten shillings each; it was as easy as that.

In the meanwhile East Street had been bombed; trading from the shop had come to a standstill, and Ethel had gone back to work at the Star Hotel behind the bar, getting more than four times Willy's pay.

At the same time Willy was able—at a price—to supply a limited but regular quantity of spirits to the Star Hotel. Where he got it from remains a mystery; no questions were ever asked.

After a while Ann was able to attend a private kindergarten—the two of them were living with her grandparents who looked after the child while her mother was working. Thus the Shauns kept their end up all through the war.

At long last it was over and Willy duly demobilized. It took him several months to settle down to civilian life. He was aware that he would have to make a big decision sooner or later and wanted time to think about it and survey his position in the antique trade. It was not until 1946, when something happened to give him the final push, that he made up his mind.

He had left the Army with the mixed feelings of relief, good riddance, and disgust at the meanness of his gratuity. Victorious England rewarding her Soldier Son!

'My God,' he said, 'if it ever happens again I *make* bullets, not stop them!'

His six years' service in the Army had left more mark on his outlook than on his appearance—still the same restless eyes, but the shock of black hair now somewhat thinner on top through continuously wearing a steel helmet during the early days of the war. That he was much fatter both in body and face was due to the regular meals rather than the quantity or quality of army food. He carried his wounded shoulder a little stiffly, but it was hardly noticeable. A good many of his colleagues would have made the most of the disability, but rather than be messed about with medical examinations for the rest of his life, let alone the business of sticking it out against medical boards whose sole purpose was to pare your pension down to the bone, Willy shrugged his wounded shoulder and in typical dealer fashion wrote it off as a bad debt—a bad debt against a country with a short memory.

Everywhere he looked business was flourishing—everybody looked prosperous except other poor mutts like himself. The column-dodgers, the clever ones, were well off; with nothing in the shops to spend it on they had been able to save quite a bit of money.

At last more luxury goods began to reappear in shop-windows as factories switched over from war to peace. The Labour Government were shouting the odds about nationalization of this and that. A good many thoughtful men were already beginning to wonder what they had been fighting for during the last six years—against the Nazis?—against dictatorship? Yet here in England was a Government legalizing the appropriation of wealth and business to which it had no moral right.

As for Willy, he was finished with politics and politicians: to him they were all tarred with the same brush, they all stood for centralized bureau-cratic control, the employment of a huge army of civil servants and the levying of heavy taxes.

He had seen enough bureaucracy and the boot-licking that went with it while he was in the Army. From now on *his* only politics were to be in favour of Willy Shaun and family. Live and let live was his code, and let the Devil take the hindmost. All his life he had been forced to fight for every penny he possessed, and had got what he had by sheer hard work and the use of his wits, the same as his father had done before him. If his business methods were not particularly honest according to some standards—well, business was business, and honest enough as far as he was concerned.

He could see which way the wind was blowing. They are not going to get a penny more out of me than I can avoid paying, he said to himself, for all these tom-fool schemes and the graft that goes with them! Land fit for heroes to live in? Bunkum! Why should I have to pay heavy income tax, purchase tax, and the rest, with money that has taken me as much as an eighty-hour week to earn, to subsidize the living standard of some lazy swine who only wants to work forty hours in a week, or who belongs to a union which forbids its members to work harder than a certain fixed rate, or someone who does not want to work at all? Why should I be forced to pay towards the upkeep and education of other people's children? I'm doing very nicely looking after my own, and no thanks to anyone.

With all this in mind Willy did not want the type of business easily 'got at' by the Inland Revenue. Trade, it seemed to him, was going to be very good for the next few years. On the other hand the cost of living was bound to rise with the unions clamouring for more money and shorter working hours.

To go on trading for any length of time in East Street would be use-less. On the other hand, to buy a fine shop in a non-industrial town, a shop like Fred Mellis had in Steading, would mean borrowing capital and a radical change in business tactics. His dream must wait. The answer was to deal entirely with other dealers. In any case it wasn't all jam selling to private customers: 'Can't make up my mind.' 'I'll think about it.' 'Can I have it on approval?' 'I'll buy it, but I can't pay for it right away.' 'I've brought this back, it won't go where I thought it would.' 'What, three pounds for *that* thing? I saw one just like it in another shop only marked a pound.' 'How much are you asking for that pair of vases in the window? Six pounds ten? Thank you! I've got a pair just like them at home and wanted to find out how much they were worth.' No, Willy decided, he wouldn't miss this sort of thing very much.

If he were to deal with the trade he would be much better off with premises just outside Torminster. A nice house with good storage sheds and an acre or two of land for privacy—in other words what he wanted was a smallholding with a low agricultural rating. This would cut out expensive town overheads and would be better for his wife and daughter. It would be easier for him, particularly in the case of storage and display of his trade goods.

At last his mind was made up for him.

All through the war the garage next door to the Shaun premises had been busy on some small aircraft component contract. Now they were back to repairing and selling cars, and were in a position to expand. The tone of East Street was improving as large multi-storied shops and buildings went up on the bomb-sites. The garage did not possess really good showrooms and it was essential for them to get hold of Willy's shop and yard so that they could build proper showrooms facing on to the street.

'That property's got to be bought,' said Tyler, the owner and managing director of the garage company. 'Could never have bought it from the old man, but I expect Willy will sell. His father would just have hung out against us out of pure cussedness, but Willy is different. He'll sell, if the price is high enough.'

Tyler had it surveyed, from the outside.

'Not worth all that much—except to you,' said the surveyor. 'Good site, but the property is in bad state. Your idea is to pull it down, I suppose?'

'That's the ultimate idea. What's it worth?'

'Before the war, five hundred; now, thanks to the Jerry bombers, about five thousand pounds in that condition. But don't hesitate too long —the multiples are on the grab in this town—you couldn't out-bid big business.'

At a chosen moment Tyler casually asked Willy if he ever thought of selling his business. His question did not catch that downy bird napping.

'S'matter of fact I've got it in mind. Had a good offer for it the other day—said I wanted time to think it over. Have to find another property for myself first.'

This took the wind straight out of Tyler's sails. All his carefully planned attack fizzled out. If someone else ever got that property it would be the end of their expansion in the street.

'How much were you offered?'

'That's my business, Mr. Tyler. Be a bit of a fool if I couldn't keep an offer private. You interested?'

Reluctantly Tyler intimated that he was.

'What is your figure for it, Shaun? We want to buy it.'

'If you want it, you bid for it,' said Willy cunningly. 'I have to bid for anything I want at a sale—you jolly well do the same.'

In the end Willy got seven thousand for it, Tyler paying all expenses.

When Ethel heard the news she could not help having a little sniff and weep into her handkerchief. She had been there sixteen years. Willy had neither weep nor sniff. He'd been there too long. He knew in which direction he was going.

The next day found him seated in the client's chair in the private office of an estate agent well known to him. In the past, between them, they had managed to pull off quite a number of rather near-the-knuckle transactions.

Their conversation was of an exceedingly delicate and private nature, not to be heard by or passed on to any member of the Inland Revenue. The parting words of Jack Earnshalle as Shaun left the office were:

'Won't be easy to find one like that, Willy, but I'll try. Can't be done in a hurry. I'll keep my ear to the ground. Not easy at all, at all.'

'I can wait. There's no immediate hurry,' said Willy.

1947 was one of the most profitable years ever known by the antique trade in general, except perhaps in the early 1920's when fabulously wealthy American millionaires had been putty in the hands of dealers who were the masters of their trade. Business everywhere was good, let alone business to do with goods that were still rationed or controlled, the spiv's stamping-ground. Black-market money, money hoarded by the tax-dodgers, and under-the-counter money, all acquired during and just after the war, was just beginning to pour out in one huge spending Niagara. Every transaction was cash, cash, cash—cheques were not acceptable. As the full flood swept past, Willy filled his own reservoirs with as much as he could catch. No matter what he bought, it sold—the good, the bad, the indifferent, and the fake. Bow-fronted chests, sideboards, tables, chairs, anything with a use, all sold with amazing rapidity to a pocket-bulging population starved of goods.

Willy was still using the shop, but more as a store than as showrooms. As he was seldom there during the daytime, private customers got the cold shoulder. In the evenings, after 9 p.m., it was different; then his colleagues in the trade called on him, and it was then that he did by far the biggest part of his business. He had most of the antiques he found by day sold the same night before he locked up. It was not unusual for dealers to call as late as midnight and quite a common occurrence to have one or two hammering on the door in the morning, long before his breakfast was ready. The demand for anything in the antique line was unending, but Willy, remembering his resourceful father, did not always choose to sell what he bought, but put aside some of the finest pieces of furniture, porcelain, and silver for his own use. He had sorted out all his father's silver, selling off what was mediocre or rubbishy and retaining the best. The scrap price of silver was now four shillings per ounce, and the value of the old man's hoard had doubled itself. Willy gave the money he made on the silver to Ethel, who banked it in her own account, thus ensuring that straightforward answers could be given to future awkward questions.

A chartered accountant now did the books. At first sight it looked as though Shaun must have been running his business at a loss, but between the two of them they got the accounts reasonably presented for income tax purposes.

One day in mid-1947 his friend Jack Earnshalle, the estate agent, telephoned.

'Yes, just right. Fifteen miles out. Oh yes, good out-houses. Yes, I think so. Owes a lot. Been trying to get his end up for a long time. No, no, definitely not. Could do, be worth your while. Yes, come round right away.' Willy replaced the receiver quietly and with deliberation. Sounded just what he was looking for.

'Going round to Jack's, dear. He's on to something. Expect me when you see me and keep any nosy parkers out of the back room. 'Bye, love!' He was gone with the door banged loudly behind him before Ethel got a chance to ask a single question.

Ten minutes later the two of them were on the way out of Torminster, Jack Earnshalle, at the wheel of his own car, heading in the direction of the moors. Jack, with his ear everlastingly to the ground, had heard of just the place for Willy, fifteen miles out from Torminster on the main road to Tormouth.

Twenty minutes later they were both looking at it from the road. The property was something more than a smallholding; it had an air about it and had obviously known better days. The house, largish and rather farm-like, was late Victorian—pseudo-Georgian with gratuitous fiddly embellishments which the architect had been unable to resist. The lawns and gardens were well arranged but sadly overgrown. Privacy was ensured in the front by two thick-clipped yew hedges on either side of the white-painted iron gate. The gravelled and weedy drive curved round in front of the house, disappearing on the other side towards some well-built out-houses and sheds.

Bit overpowering for me, thought Willy, as he pushed open the reluctant squeaky gate.

The owner, Captain Terence Algernon Vestere, came out to meet them as they were halfway up the drive. He was a gentleman—that was obvious despite his shabby tweedy clothes and worn, harassed features. 'I'm Vestere. Are you Earnshalle?' This to Willy, who, with a negative inclination of his head, indicated his friend. Army type, hard up, hands known rough work, he thought. Toffee-nosed family background by the look of him. Will depend on how hard up he is whether he'll do business my way. One of the 'can't-let-the-jolly-old-party-down' type.

Vestere took them over the house. Willy was not particularly impressed. Seemed to be a maze of long passages with innumerable doors leading to goodness knew where. Cost a small fortune to decorate, he told himself. Won't suit Ethel all that much. H'm! Two good rooms in the front. Show the furniture off well. Panelled ceilings and walls. Venetian blinds and casement shutters—just what the doctor ordered, except the odd hundred quid to decorate each room!

Willy poked and prodded here and there. The woodwork everywhere seemed to be sound. Jack also had his eyes open and nostrils quivering for dry rot. The whole house was well built. The outside was somewhat ravaged by the weather and showed signs of neglect but there was nothing seriously wrong anywhere—not even the odd woodworm hole. Upstairs the bedrooms, five in all, carried out the same pattern as below. Sanitary arrangements were old-fashioned, and there would be a very long walk in the middle of the night for anyone sleeping in the back bedroom over the kitchen.

The out-houses were Willy's main interest. What had once been a large stable and carriage house was now converted into a garage for two cars and a corn-and-meal store, with straw and litter in the loft running over both granary and garage. Brick-built and slate-roofed, Willy noted, and estimated that a building such as this, without the quality of materials and workmanship, would cost well over a thousand pounds to erect nowadays.

At the rear of this building was a newer shed, lower but much longer, stretching a good hundred feet down towards the wall at the bottom of the yard. Once inside, its purpose was self-explanatory. Five large chicken incubators, each in its own separate wire-meshed compound, were now standing sullenly idle. Willy noted that this shed also was supplied with electricity.

Like many officers and gentlemen, survivors of the 1914–18 war, facing reduced incomes, Terence Vestere had thought poultry farming looked easy; he intended going in for things in a big way—the scientific way. He soon realized that poultry farming is not child's play, and had he been wise he would have cut his losses and sold out to another sucker almost as soon as he had bought himself in, but he did not like to be beaten and was not afraid of hard work. He struggled on and on, barely making a living. If he had fiddled his returns like many another sensible man, the tide might have turned for him. As it was he ended the Second World War in worse shape than he had been before it. His wife's illness had added to his debts and her death left him a saddened and embittered man.

A good deal of all this Willy guessed, more or less, as he took in the rusting wire-netted pens, the gates off their hinges, the hundred or so hens that were left, and the old-fashioned incubators that were too out-of-date to sell.

He looked across the field—at the rotting posts vainly trying to hold up the rusty caved-in wire netting, at the drinking troughs and accessories already half buried in grass and clumps of stinging nettles. The property was just what he had in mind, but what could he do with all this land and clap-trap on it? Let it off to someone perhaps?—not a bad idea.

The tour of inspection over, they all returned to the house. Willy and Jack had an earnest conversation for quite a few minutes.

'What is it worth, Jack?'

'Not everyone's house, Willy, but it could be turned into flats. I don't think you'd ever have much difficulty in selling it again. It's not that big, and the garage and sheds are a good asset. You can look on the land as an investment. Good future building site there—absolutely ideal, with the main road here in front and the village road running parallel at the bottom of the field. He wants five thousand five hundred pounds—reasonable enough!'

'What do you think he would take? He's hard up, you say.'

'I don't really come into this at all, Willy. Toosey and Toosey are supposed to be handling it for him. Briggs the farmer over at Tiddleport told me about it.'

'Present company excepted, Jack, but I don't like estate agents. I must buy it direct or not at all. I'll see you right on it. Ethel won't think much of not being consulted over this. She was furious when I sold the East Street property without telling her what I was up to—didn't know myself if it comes to that—just had to make up my mind then and there.'

They joined Vestere in the large lounge. To Willy's disappointment there wasn't an antique in the place worth asking the price of. Vestere was very reserved. He intended to sell, but now faced with a possible buyer he realized what a wrench it would be. He poured out the whisky and Willy began to feel somewhat uncomfortable. Whisky in the drawing-room—this kind of thing wasn't much in his line.

However, he knew what he wanted so in he went baldheaded.

'Mr. Vestere, sir. I understand you want five thousand five hundred pounds for this property.'

Vestere nodded, and Willy continued:

'I never deal with agents, don't trust them. Mr Earnshalle is one, as you know, but he is a personal friend, here in that capacity to advise me. I am prepared to buy this property straight away. You can cancel out any agents and save yourself the commission. I'm prepared to give you the sum you want, without haggling over the price, on two conditions.'

At Willy's elbow Jack Earnshalle gasped. He had never known Shaun agree to pay what he was asked! Dammit, it was a cinch it could have been bought for the straight five thousand!

Vestere hesitated. He did not wish to run word with Toosey and Toosey, but so far they had not produced any likely buyer—just a number of people looking round for the sake of being plain nosy. If he did as this man Shaun was suggesting he would probably receive a bill for valuation of the property.

'Yes, Mr Shaun. I am prepared to sell; but what are the conditions?'

'The first is, sir, that the property is to be conveyed to me for the sum of three thousand pounds and I will give you in cash the balance of two thousand five hundred for fixtures, fittings, and all outlyings on the land. In return for this sum I want a receipt for two hundred pounds. The second one is that you agree never to divulge the truth about the latter part of the transaction.'

Vestere gave Willy a long thoughtful look. Forty years ago he would have kicked this man's backside, but things were different today. The man obviously wanted to unload some undeclared cash and goodness only knows he could do with it. Being a True Blue he regarded any man successfully diddling the present Labour Government almost as a hero. It didn't make much difference to him how the money came. Most of it would go—bank overdraft, doctor's bills unpaid, hundreds of other bills, and, last of all, settling day with the bookmakers.

'That's all very well, Mr Shaun, but once the property has been conveyed, how do I know you will pay the two thousand five hundred pounds?'

'Easy. You can make a point of signing the conveyance in your solicitor's office. I will meet you outside, give you the money and we go in together for your signature on the dotted line. O.K.?'

Vestere nodded. It all seemed satisfactory. Not that he liked doing business that way. This, he supposed, was how people got on in life nowadays. He sighed and held out his hand. Willy had his smallholding.

Driving back to Torminster, Jack laughed. 'You're a bloody crafty one. You shook me rigid when you agreed to pay his price. How come you got so much cash?'

'You ought to know. John Bellman was telling me that you were in the knockout the other day as well—at one of your own sales too. I'm surprised at you, Jack.'

'He's a downright liar, that man. All I had was a small present. I had nothing to do with any settlement afterwards. I didn't trot the bidding up on one lot, that's all.'

Willy did a long calculation on the way home—one thousand two hundred pounds cash in the bank, current account, all tax paid, eight hundred pounds of stock declared, undeclared another one thousand. Private hoard of cash—about three thousand pounds. Father's silver and gold—don't know, must be worth two thousand five hundred pounds, and finally the seven thousand from old Grissly Tyler in his deposit account. Leave four thousand pounds in deposit, and five hundred pounds loose cash. This deal has put a hole in that three thousand quid all right. . . . 'Take some making up again, knockout or no knockout. . . .' He muttered the last few words audibly.

'You still on about it, Willy? I tell you I don't go into the knockout, especially at one of my own sales.'

'No, Jack lad, I was only talking to myself. I'm worried. I don't know how Ethel is going to take this packet. But what else could I do?

C

No good letting the grass grow under your feet on a deal like that. It had to be bought. You come home with me. She can't fly off the handle quite so much in front of you. Give her a bit of time to think things over. By the way, Jack, what do I owe you for this afternoon?'

'I leave it to you—can't make a professional charge.'

'Thirty pounds cash be all right?'

'Sure, that's fine with me. Didn't do all that much.'

Willy passed over six five-pound notes—keep old Jack nice and sweet—never know when he may come in useful again.

Ethel was a little overwhelmed when the two of them recounted the day's happenings. Willy noted a few danger signals, but his wife was completely won over after Jack's description of the house and property.

'Be living in proper style from now on, Ethel. You will soon be hobnobbing with all the County folk. Hope you don't forget your old friends.' He gave a broad wink.

3   The Ring, the Knockout, and the Settlement

One June morning, when he had been about three years settled in his new home, Willy drove to a sale in Caverton, a small town eighteen miles from Torminster. The morning was fresh; a haze lay on the water-meadows golden with buttercups, the trees were at their loveliest, still alive with different shades of green before settling down to the darker uniformity of summer. And always, to the west, there were the moors, their astonishing shapes rising and tumbling away as he sped along the twisting road. The mellow stone cottages, honey-coloured in the sun, delighted Willy's eye for their own sake; he was well used now to apprais-ing the lasting values, the harmony and proportion, in the work of all good craftsmen; and there was always the exciting possibility of treasure within, a pair of rare cockfighting chairs, a yew-tree corner cupboard, some Swansea or Nantgarw china, its value unsuspected by the owners— the chance of a lifetime that colours the more sober day-dreams of every antique dealer. But though, in a general way, Willy took in all these pleasant influences, feeling that they reflected his own sense of well-being and growing prosperity, his mind, as always, was running ahead of him, thinking of the sale and what he might expect to get from it, thinking

35

about his fellow dealers, the auctioneers, the trade, more particularly about the ring, the knockout, and the settlement.

Most people who attend auction sales where antiques are listed in the catalogue are aware of the existence of the ring. There are those who condemn all antique dealers for what is reputed to go on after a sale, without realizing that not all dealers belong to the ring. It is a matter of choice, governed by financial strength, personal integrity, and perhaps the ability to buy antiques from sources other than antique sales.

What happens—and there are variations on the procedure, which has been common practice for the last fifty years—is something like this: a group of dealers who have made an unwritten agreement not to bid against each other get together after a sale to re-auction among themselves goods that they have just bought; this auction is called the 'knockout'. As the bidding proceeds dealer after dealer is forced to retire from the circle as the lot which is being 'knocked out' goes beyond the value that each man places on it. The paying out at the end, which is called the 'settlement', is done in a complicated way which ensures that all who bid and are forced to retire get paid proportionately according to the amount they have bid up to the point of their retirement. (In fact all these terms are used interchangeably.) Round after round takes place, those whose knowledge, courage, or financial strength take them into the final round making the most money. The last man—the highest bidder—pays out to all his colleagues the difference between his highest bid and the money originally paid for the lot under the hammer—and incidentally the difference between its true value and what the seller got for it at the sale.

But Willy, as he slowed down to pass over a little seventeenth-century bridge on the outskirts of Caverton, was not concerned with the public interest. He was wondering, with a mild sense of grievance, why all the fuss was made about antique dealers, and the ring. What about the farmers? As he well knew, a good ring always ran at cattle sales, or when a hayrick or farm implements were being sold. And the goings-on of the car dealers were even worse—and, come to that, what business ever existed without a ring of some sort? Price-rigging, price-fixing—the big manufacturers not hesitating to cut off supplies from some misguided small retailer who dared to sell their commodities under the stipulated minimum price—a ring unobtrusive but gigantic. And what about local council and Government contracts? Why was it nearly always announced that the lowest tender might not necessarily be accepted? Wasn't it possible that the contracts were 'knocked out' between the various contractors?

The toffee-nosed attitude of the auctioneer in Caverton was a constant source of irritation to the local antique trade. It seemed to them that the only ones who made any easy money out of antiques were the auctioneers. There certainly wasn't much to be made from things acquired in the knockout—the business was far too cut-throat.

As for the auctioneer, all he had to do was arrange delivery of the goods to the sale-room, charge the customer for it, stick on a lot number, publish a catalogue, sit on the selling rostrum with a clerk, shout the odds and drop his hammer at the appropriate moment—sometimes on his own bid through choice or misfortune, depending on whether he wished to acquire the item for himself or was just caught out trotting it up against someone else. For this he or his firm received a commission of between three and four shillings in the pound.

Another point was that they accepted no responsibility for damage or mis-description in the catalogue. Time and time again antique dealers would come from all parts only to find at the end of perhaps a two-hundred-mile journey that the 'Chinese Chippendale Period Mahogany Silver Table, with pierced fretted gallery, standing on square pierced fretted legs' was some horrible Victorian monstrosity and not even a silver table at that. It was no good for a dealer at a distance to ring up a local man for information. Even if he was told the truth he would not be able to believe it, thinking that he was simply being put off a good thing.

Yes, Willy decided, the auctioneer had an easy and remunerative profession.

On the other hand the antique dealer had the public bidding against him, sometimes the auctioneer, and all his fellow traders. He had to back his knowledge with his own money. Sometimes after haulage, repairs, and having his capital tied up for weeks, months, and even years, he made less profit out of any given item than the auctioneer.

Willy arrived in time to check over the contents of the sale, which he had previously viewed, before it began.

Lot 107, he thought—wonder if anyone else here knows the truth about it? If not, someone's likely to get a 'hot lot' dropped on him! Lot 107 was catalogued 'Large blue-and-white Delft Flower Vase'. It was nothing of the sort; it was a water-font, with typical Italian Urbino-type decoration. Though 'blue-and-white' has gone out of fashion, an early specimen of this type in perfect condition can be worth quite a bit of money. Two days ago in Tormouth Willy had bumped into Gaveeney, a London dealer of a wide reputation with an outstanding knowledge of continental pottery and porcelain, had given him details of the font, and the great man was interested enough to come up for a look at it. His only remark as he set eyes on it was: 'Wasted journey, Shaun— nineteenth-century copy.' And that was that.

As Willy moved round the sale-room he was annoyed to notice Peter Nebbing watching his every movement out of the corner of his eye. What a pest that chap was! Peter was a hanger-on of the local antique world who made up in shrewdness and cunning for what he lacked in knowledge. If he observed a number of dealers all looking at the same lot, he too would have a look-see and mark the lot in his catalogue as something to be watched.

I'll fix him, thought Willy, struck by a wonderful idea. The porter had been blabbing to all and sundry that Gaveeney had been up to view the sale. He turned to Lot 107, marked it plainly in the margin '£95' and underneath in large letters, 'Gaveeney.'

Turning his attention to some rubbishy bits of china he put down his catalogue ready for Peter, who by now was standing right by him. The opportunity was too good to miss. . . . Peter took a quick look. . . . What he saw made him blink—couldn't be any mistake about it though— 'Lot 107—£95—Gaveeney!'

'Hallo, Peter!' said Willy. 'Found any hidden bargains?'

Peter made some noncommittal answer and wended his way up the sale-room in quiet excitement. Gosh!—he'd show 'em in the knockout! Taking the porter on one side he got the answer he wanted: Yes, Shaun had come in with Gaveeney yesterday for a private view. Peter found his pal Charlie Mathion, and the context of their whispered conversation put a light in Charlie's eye as well.

When the sale started there were about twenty of the ring in the sale-room, scattered about at the back of the room in no way arousing the curiosity and suspicion of the mixed crowd to whom stuffy sale-rooms are always an attraction. Ropey Stringer, Mabel and Hugh Twerleet who owned the only antique shop in the town, 'Crash' Wilson, Reg Bardon. . . . Willy greeted them all with a nod. The Twerleets were an ill-assorted couple; Mabel, a loud-mouthed frizzy-haired woman in her forties whose stockings were always laddered, dwarfed and dominated her husband, though she would fly at the throat of anyone who picked on him. Ropey Stringer with his usual sarcasm affirmed that on their honeymoon each got such a shock that they changed sex. Ropey, a thin, cadaverous dealer inclined to peptic ulcers, was known for his sarcasm, his ginger hair, his secrecy about his own business, and the way he rubbed everyone up the wrong way. 'Crash' Wilson was a 'knockabout' or general dealer. He had no right to fly the 'Antiques' banner but was generally considered as useful by those who stood above him. His forte lay in catching unsuspecting householders off their guard. After tapping on the door and querying 'Anything for sale?' he usually managed to insinuate his long, rather weaselly body through the gap in the door. It was his pathetically appealing expression, his respectable worn grey worsted suit (always bought second-hand), which did the trick.

These were the four locals. Among the other dealers the biggest contrast was between Reg Bardon, who owned the highest-class antique shop in the district, and the Tiddingtons, father and son. Apart from being extra tall, Reg could be recognized anywhere from behind because of his ears which stuck out like an old bull elephant's about to charge. Reg was a gentleman, more or less, with a good business and a private income inherited from his father, and always managed to look one. Tiddington senior, a pint-sized beady-eyed little begger with a shock of unkempt black hair, who invariably wore a blue striped flannel shirt without a collar and who irritated his cronies by his habit of sniffing and spitting when things went against him, missed most opportunities through being too suspicious and cunning. He was never seen without his son, who was so unlike him—fair, tall, fresh-complexioned—that Ropey, with his ear for a bit of village scandal, swore he was the spit-and-image of the local baker.

Of the twenty dealers present only about ten had legitimate antique businesses and among these Willy and his friend Tom Elliot were fairly high in the hierarchy. The others were, like Charlie Mathion and Peter Nebbing, 'hangers-on'—the term for small fry who are only in a settlement so that they can bid up to a certain point and retire with their share of the knockout money, but have no intention of buying any lots. They were only tolerated by the others because sometimes they were useful for what was known as 'plugging' and they made it their business to find out every detail of every sale for miles around, their freely imparted information usually being reliable.

As the biggest dealer, Reg Bardon on behalf of his colleagues and himself had purchased nearly every antique lot at the Caverton sale.

He became chairman of this particular settlement, with Levenstein to do the clerking.

After the sale they had all unobtrusively edged their way round to the back of the sale-rooms and gathered in one of the cowsheds.

Reg called down the catalogue.

' "Lot 18. Bow-front chest of drawers." I bought it. Cost eighteen pounds under the hammer. Who wants it?'

On this lot there had been only lukewarm private opposition and no trade opposition throughout the sale. This was an easy one. Everyone present was able to appraise the value of the chest of drawers exactly—worth twenty-eight pounds to any of the dealers—to sell in their shops for about thirty-three to thirty-five pounds. All twenty claimed it. A rough circle was formed and the bidding started. Ropey was standing on the left-hand side of Reg Bardon who had bought the chest, so Ropey had to begin the bidding, which always goes clockwise round the circle. Ropey put 'Five shillings on', and so it went on round. Everyone had to advance the bidding in turn, and everyone knew that when it reached 'Ten pounds on' (bringing the total price to twenty-eight pounds) the bidding would stop.

As the bidding proceeded, Peter Nebbing, standing next to Ropey, realized that the final price would fall somewhere near his position. He didn't want to buy the chest of drawers but wanted to stay in the bidding as long as possible so he advanced twenty-five shillings. This was intended to clear the ultimate 'dropping price' of twenty-eight pounds well away from his position on the clock.

Tom Elliot, when his turn came, advanced fifteen shillings to put it back again near Peter Nebbing, at the same time giving Willy and Reg a broad wink. It was known to all that Peter, being a 'hanger-on', didn't want to be landed with the chest of drawers. He had no shop to sell it in. The bidding was just becoming interesting when Reg Bardon filled the gap.

'Ten guineas on. If anyone wants it over that price they can have it.'

He wanted it for his shop and as it was 'there' in price, now standing at eighteen pounds purchase price and ten guineas added on, no one else showed any inclination to bid again, so they all 'faded'. Reg paid over ten guineas in notes to 'Levvy', who had made a list of all present. In this case everyone had been in the ring until the last bid so all were entitled to an equal share. Twenty divided into ten guineas was ten shillings for each man and ten shillings over to go into Levvy's pocket for all the trouble involved in clerking.

Reg continued: 'Next lot. "Lot 63. Three copper measures and a warming-pan." '

At this moment both Willy and Tom Elliot moved round to where Tiddington was standing. Tiddy, as he was called, had quietly purchased Lot 51 by bidding with his left hand while standing against the left-hand wall of the sale-room. Only the auctioneer could see his bid and, realizing the bids were secret, had not named the buyer in the usual loud voice.

'I say, Tiddywinks,' said Willy, *sotto voce*, '*you* bought Lot 51. Tom and I are claiming it. No need to let the rest know about it. We'll settle that lot afterwards.'

Tiddy was downhearted and surprised. He thought he had a superb little seventeenth-century brass tinder-box, which had rubbed shoulders with about seven other bits of brass rubbish in the same lot, all to himself for the sum of thirty-five shillings. Unfortunately for him the other two had also seen it and noting the quarter the bidding was coming from had marked their man, allowing him to buy it without fuss.

" 'Three copper measures and a warming-pan,' " continued Reg, completely unaware that a lot worth seven pounds ten shillings and bought for thirty-five shillings had escaped him and all the others except three. 'Cost six pounds ten shillings under the hammer. Anyone want them?'

Three cans at two pounds each, top price, left the warming-pan at ten shillings, to earn a profit of two pounds on the deal—not worth touching. No one claimed that lot.

Next came the water-font, Lot 107—a real gambling one. Nearly everyone there knew that Gaveeney had viewed the sale beforehand; and, as Shaun had been able to get the font under the hammer for four pounds ten shillings against a woman who fancied it, it was obvious that Gaveeney had not left a price with the porter or the auctioneer so that they could buy it for him. Someone among the dealers present must be acting for the great man, waiting to buy it in the settlement. Gaveeney did not come down from London for nothing, they reasoned, and there was no doubt it was the font he had come to look at. He himself would not appear at the sale since his presence would have given every dealer the knowledge that a good lot was in the offing—knowledge that dealers are all too quick to take advantage of. He had probably left his price with the person who had given him the tip-off.

Reg cleared his throat. 'Come on now, Lot 107. Shaun bought it. Cost four pounds ten shillings. Who wants it?'

Reg felt himself on very unsafe ground regarding this font. Having classified it as 'modern' when he first saw it, the only reason inducing him to change his mind was the fact that Shaun seemed to be interested in it. Shaun very seldom put a foot wrong. Had the font been 'modern', Shaun would certainly not be wanting it. Arty-arty decorative pieces were not in his line. Then there was Gaveeney. . . . Oh well, he thought, better have a gamble on it. If it's an old one it must be worth fifty quid. Everyone claimed it and in a tense atmosphere the little group formed up the circle again.

'Cost four pound ten—over to you, Tiddy.'

'Five bob on,' said Tiddy.

Willy jumped on him. 'Come off it, you'll bid decently on a lot like this or not at all. One-pound bids or get out of it. Can't afford to waste time like that.'

There was a murmur of assent and the bidding went the round of the circle, coming to Willy at nineteen pounds on, the complete cost now being twenty-three pounds ten.

Willy did not hesitate—'Twenty pounds.'

'That's enough for me,' said Tiddy, who was supposed to make the next advance. He was no strong gambler, and a pound in his pocket meant more to him than 'holding' a hot lot which he would not readily be able to sell.

This was the signal for a general fade-out from the bidding by the small fry.

'No one else wants it, do they?' enquired Willy, rather giving the impression that he was anxious to get on with the next lot, and retain the font for himself.

'I do,' said Tom. He was quite prepared to have a bigger gamble.

'I'm in,' said Reg.

'And me,' from Ropey.

'So are we,' came simultaneously from Peter Nebbing and Charlie Mathion.

Tom's jaw dropped and Reg looked as though he could hardly believe his ears. Peter and Charlie Mathion were two of the worst 'hangers-on' for miles around. They nearly always contented themselves with shillings rather than pounds on each lot and were usually the first to fade from the bidding in the first round. It was almost unbelievable for them to come into the second round of a knockout.

Ah!—thought Tom and Reg—Peter Nebbing had Gaveeney's price and was putting his pal Charlie in as a plug. Charlie had been told to bid until Peter gave him a nudge. If he ended up with a fiver or more on this particular lot, Peter would take most of it from him, allowing him to keep perhaps thirty bob of it for himself.

Meanwhile Levvy had divided the twenty pounds given to him by Willy. The division was easy. There were twenty dealers. Twenty pounds had been advanced and given to him. Everyone had a pound note to come.

The ones who had finished with the font were paid out and told by Reg in no uncertain fashion to 'B—— well get out of hearing' as the business in the second round was no concern of those who had now finished.

Levvy intimated that he was 'out' but volunteered to carry on as treasurer.

'Come on,' said Willy. 'Can't waste all day. I'm holding it at twenty pounds on—over to you, Tom. Two-pound bids from now on.'

A smaller circle had now been formed and Tom was next to Willy.

'Twenty-two pounds'—Tom. 'Twenty-four'—Ropey. 'Twenty-six' —Reg. 'Twenty-eight'—Mathion. 'Thirty'—Peter. 'Thirty-two'— Willy.

The bidding went round yet again, Willy bidding forty-six pounds and Tom quickly following at forty-eight pounds.

'That's enough for me,' said Reg. The total cost was now over fifty pounds. A gamble was a gamble, but not over that amount for something he knew nothing about. It was high enough for Ropey, who also said he had finished.

Tom was thus left holding it for 'forty-eight pounds on', having advanced twenty-eight pounds in the second round. There had been six men in this round. Twenty-eight pounds divided by six came out at four pounds ten each, with the odds going to Levvy for his trouble. Tom handed over the twenty-eight pounds, Reg and Ropey each receiving five pounds ten—four pounds ten from the second and one pound from the first round.

'I'm still in,' said Willy.

'And so are we,' from Peter and Charlie.

The four of them started bidding again.

'Fifty pounds'—Mathion. 'Fifty-two'—Peter. 'Fifty-four'—Willy. Tom hesitated. By staying in that far, without even bidding, if he retired he could collect another thirty shillings without the risk of getting 'landed' with a font for fifty-eight pounds ten, a lump of pottery of a sort he didn't know about. However, Shaun seemed strong enough. He must know something; and Peter had Gaveeney's price—that was now certain.

'Fifty-six'—Tom. 'Fifty-eight'—Mathion, now very red in the face with nervous tension. 'Sixty' from Peter. 'Sixty-two'—Willy, without any hesitation. Again Tom hesitated, but not for long—'Sixty-four.' 'Sixty-six'—Mathion. 'Sixty-eight'—Peter.

'That's enough for me,' said Willy, elation welling up inside him.

'And me,' echoed Tom, mightily relieved that it had not been 'dropped' on him.

Willy was itching to get outside and tell Tom all about it. Tell Reg as well, for that matter. He had done it at last—brought off the seemingly impossible—dropped a lot worth no more than five pounds on to Peter Nebbing for seventy-two pounds ten shillings! Peter had had it coming to him for a long time.

Peter was looking at him with concern and amazement. Why had Shaun dropped out like that? Suddenly Peter had the answer. Of course! Shaun thought that four were too many and it would be better policy to bluff the others out of the bidding, then quietly 'settle' it between the two of them afterwards. Only common sense—more to share out. He caught Willy's eye at last and gave him a knowing wink.

He heard his name called; Levvy was demanding the sixty-eight pounds from him. His roll of notes was left very thin after he'd handed it over.

Levvy was busy with his calculations. Clerking was by no means an easy job, especially when it came to a big sale. Willy was also doing a few calculations; it was always worth doing a check on Levvy's arithmetic. Levvy quite frequently made a 'mistake' in his divisions, and paid out each man a pound note less than he was owed. He had never been known to do it in reverse.

Another twenty pounds had been 'put on' in the third and last round between four—Peter, Charlie, Tom, and Willy. That was five pounds each. All these four had one pound to come from the first round, four pounds ten from the second and five pounds from the third round. This last was hard luck on him for it was an exact division with no overs. The twenty pounds previously paid by Willy was returned, together with his share. Tom likewise received back his twenty-eight pounds plus share —Peter now having provided the complete amount. The business of the font had been concluded.

Willy pocketed the ten guineas, which he had made merely by bidding in the settlement.

The other four lots were then dealt with in the same way, Reg Bardon holding all four. He wanted goods rather than 'knockout money'—a shop that is always empty is a bad advertisement.

Willy collected another six pounds ten shillings from these four lots, two pounds from three of them and four pounds ten shillings in a straight fight between himself and Reg, no one else claiming a country-made mahogany Chippendale Gainsborough-type armchair for which Reg had paid twenty-two pounds under the hammer. Willy put on eight pounds ten shillings but Reg took it away at nine pounds on, making the chair cost thirty-one pounds. Willy had reckoned it twenty-five pounds so let it go. Reg paid out half of nine pounds to Willy, so the chair actually cost him twenty-two pounds buying price and four pounds ten shillings paid out to Shaun—twenty-six pounds ten in all—one pound ten more than Willy's final price.

That concluded the settlement as far as everyone was concerned, apart from three men with heads down in a little group, already settling the matter of one small brass tinder-box. Willy put on three pounds, took a pound note, and came out, leaving the other two still at it.

Considering the poor amount of stuff in the sale, the day had not been a bad one after all. Willy had collected eighteen pounds ten shillings cash and was not left holding anything. He regretted leaving the bow-front but at twenty-eight pounds ten shillings it would hardly pay to handle. The most to be expected from the trade would be thirty pounds. Reg was welcome to it. He would have to spend at least another two pounds ten shillings to put it in shop-selling order.

Seeing Peter bearing down on him and guessing what was in his mind he cut him short.

'Oh, Peter. I've just come down from the auctioneer's clerk's office. I have transferred my purchase of Lot 107 to your name. You held the lot so you can settle the account.'

Looks of astonishment, disbelief, and finally sheer dismay chased across Peter's face.

'But I thought you had——' He stopped short, realizing he could not add: 'Gaveeney's price.' He was utterly dazed. He had paid out sixty-eight pounds. Sixty-eight pounds! Admittedly he had drawn six pounds back from Charlie, so it had cost him sixty-two pounds less his own share of ten guineas, making a net cost of fifty-one pounds ten, but not including the four pounds ten he would have to pay the auctioneer. What was his wife going to say when he got home with that font and told her he'd been 'landed' with it for fifty-five pounds? Perhaps he would not have to lose very much on it—after all, both Shaun and Elliot had reckoned it nearly seventy. What was Shaun up to? Double-dealing with Gaveeney?

'Well, Peter, it's not every day you hold a pricey lot. Good luck with it,' said Willy, making off in Tom's direction.

Peter wandered round and round. He just could not believe it yet. Where was Gaveeney's ninety-five pounds? Ninety-five pounds? Could it have been seventy-five? A badly drawn seven could be mistaken for a nine. That's what it was. Shaun had a price of seventy-five pounds, and apart from the odd fifty shillings that price had been reached. Oh well, it wasn't so bad after all. If Gaveeney was still interested he could have it for a lot less than seventy-five.

Judging by the roars of laughter coming from the entrance to the cattle yard he was missing a good joke, but he wasn't in the mood for jokes.

Willy had told his tale.

Tom nearly had hysterics, and Reg laughed so much he had to run for the 'Gents'.

'Oh blimey,' Tom was saying, 'I wouldn't be in that poor so-and-so's shoes when he gets home and tells that bitch of a wife about it. Haw, haw, haw!'

Tom was still perspiring slightly over the thought that he had been in the same lot up to his neck.

'Think of it—a dud font not worth a bid over a five-pound note wrapped round his neck for sixty quid. Oh, my hat! That'll learn him, boy! Your nerves must be like cast-iron, Willy.'

Willy laughed. 'Just think, Tom! You were holding it yourself for forty-eight at the end of the second round!'

Tom looked uncomfortable.

'I was following *you*. If I'd known what was in the wind I wouldn't 've touched it, of course. Oh, by the way, have you seen the catalogue of Reuthen House? Some good lots there by the look of it—get all the London boys down for that sale.'

'When is it?'

'Week after next. Three days. Wednesday, Thursday, and Friday. View days on Monday and Tuesday—London auctioneer got the sale— Rooke, Claude, and Barter. All the nobs will be there—always are at that kind of sale. Won't be able to get inside the bally place. Hope it rains all the week.'

'See if you can get me a catalogue from one of the agents, Tom. If you are going over to view on Monday you might as well call for me and we can go over it together. Two heads are better than one. How about standing in together?'

They had done this before at important sales. By and large Tom's knowledge was better than Willy's, especially with furniture, but Willy was far more astute when it came to the settlement. Tom could judge the proper value of any given lot, but Willy, when it came to gambling over and above that value in order to make an extra pound or two, seemed possessed of a sixth sense which told him how far other men with the same idea were prepared to go. He very seldom got landed with an over-valued lot but nearly always managed to get out just before others had reached their limit.

This partnership was beneficial to both and they were as near to being friends as antique dealers could be.

'O.K., Willy. It's quite a time since we had a good bat against the London crowd.'

4 View Day

On the following Tuesday Tom called early in the morning and on they went together in his car to view the sale at Reuthen House.

A death in the family was responsible for the sale. Rather than part with money well invested in shares, the house and contents, which could no longer be satisfactorily maintained owing to the heavy death-duties, were being sold to pay them—and what a sale it was!

'Strike me pink, Tom! Just look at all those cars.'

They had turned in through the main gates where the usual 'To the Sale' signpost stuck in the hedge on the opposite side of the road was pointing. Willy viewed the long row of cars parked up the main drive.

'Always the same, Tom. Half of 'em don't want to buy anything. Only here because it's the right thing to do. Idle curiosity and a social event—that is what it will be. Good epidemic of sale fever too, no doubt. Just look at that view, Tom—down there towards the river. This must have been a beautiful park once upon a time.'

They were now up to the house—a fine, stone-built, early-Georgian mansion.

The place was like an anthill; people crawling here, poking there, prying, laughing, and talking. By the look of the gents' natty tweeds and the women's fashion parade, Willy's summing up was near enough correct. This type of sale was a dealer's nightmare. There would be no rhyme or reason in the bidding. Quite ordinary commercial antiques, such as bedside commodes, would make about double the price being asked for the same thing in local antique shops.

This was bad for the small local dealer for two reasons. First because he could not hope to buy anything at the sale and afterwards because he found it difficult to get his local customers to accept down-to-earth commercial prices for such things if he was trying to make a private purchase. Having made his offer the answer was: 'Oh! I couldn't accept such a low figure. Why, at the so-and-so sale they made more than double that price.'

For once the catalogue was more or less correct in its descriptions. So it should have been, seeing that five shillings was charged for it.

It took the two of them the whole day, not stopping for lunch, to view all the things. Both Tom and Willy priced their catalogues separately, for comparison afterwards. Beautiful pieces, some of them—completely beyond their reckoning. Some of the London boys would be in their element. Most of the furniture was of the early-Georgian period, although the walnut and the later Hepplewhite and Sheraton periods were well represented. It was obvious to anyone that the early-Chippendale ball-and-claw stuff was going to make some money. It was superb both in quality and condition.

At no time were they able to get into the library to look at a library table and two pairs of library steps. It was packed tight with scavenging book dealers, all clambering up and over the shelves like a lot of monkeys in a monkey-house.

Tom stopped in front of a piece of furniture in one of the corridors. They had inspected it earlier but Tom wanted another look.

Lot No. 227. Continental Mahogany Side-table with shaped front, five drawers, carved scrolled undercarriage with centre carved shell, standing on cabriole legs terminating in square block feet. 4 ft. 8 in. wide.

'What have you got this one marked at, Willy?'
'Let's see. Lot 227. Sixty-five pounds—good export lot. Looks like Italiana to me.'

Tom came closer.

D

'It's a Yank. I'm sure of it—see that shape—typical, and look at the scrollwork and shell—Philadelphia or Boston written all over it—English Colonial period. A good many of them will miss it stuck here in this dark corridor. It will top the five hundred mark easy. I'm game, Willy. What about you?'

Willy was carefully studying the side-table. Tom was quite right. The piece had a bit of Dutch influence about it—might have been made by a Dutch cabinet-maker in America. This influence was probably responsible for its being catalogued as 'Continental'—surprising for a firm like R.C. and B. to make a mistake, but Tom was right.

'Good job it comes under the hammer on the first day. Give us a better chance. Let's get away from the darned thing. If any of the smart boys see us turning it inside out the whole wide world will know all about it.'

They moved on into another room.

'Hallo, Willy. Hallo, Tom. How's the game?'

'Why, it's Wally! How goes it your end? We can't grumble down here. Trade is pretty good. Think there will be much doing tomorrow?'

'Never seen so many private people—place is lousy with them. By the way, Willy—how the devil did you do it?'

'How the devil did I do what?'

'Why, land that bum lot on to Peter Nebbing for seventy quid? Not often you can catch one of that breed. You were in it too, weren't you, Tom?'

'Yes,' said Tom, moving awkwardly. It still gave him an uncomfortable feeling when he thought of himself gaily 'holding' the font for forty-eight pounds in the second round.

'What I like about our trade is that if anyone is in danger of slipping down the drain with a lot wrapped round his neck all his friends gather round to stamp on his fingers to make sure that he does. Peter will be trying to flog that font all over the place, but every dealer here knows about it already—doesn't give the bloke a chance, and a good job too. I wish I could put one like that over on a few up my way.'

'Seen anything worth the money, Wally?'

'Plenty, but there won't be much knockout money coming—Goldensky's here.'

'H'm, that means hefty prices left on the auctioneer's book. Why doesn't that man settle?—makes me sick—just pours money into the lap of the auctioneer.'

The porcelain was displayed in the 'French Room' on trestle tables running in three lines down the centre of the room and along the walls. Here was all the good stuff; the rest was out in the kitchens and sculleries at the back of the house.

'Haven't done much reckoning in here, Tom. How can you reckon the value of pairs of Chelsea figures? At one sale they will make two hundred pounds and at another a similar pair will top seven hundred pounds.'

'That all depends on who puts them in the sale. Some of the lads wangle their own stuff into this kind of sale, if they know the family well enough. They can then run it up like blazes in the hope that some sucker will put in a bid. Also, you have to remember that if a dealer has recently sold them to a customer for a high figure and they come into the sale-rooms, he cannot afford to see them knocked down for a very much smaller sum—not policy—bad for his business and reputation. Again, if these Chelsea figures belonged to a chap with a title they'd be worth more than if they didn't. You can't put a value on these things.

'It's just the same with pictures, Tom. Thank goodness there are none here for us to be worrying over. One of the porters told me they have all been sent up to the London sale-rooms. The family are keeping nearly all the silver.'

After another look round at the loaded tables they decided to give the porcelain up as a bad job. There was too much there to take it all in and half the items were beyond their reckoning.

'Let the china boys sort it out, Tom. We'll watch the bidding and see who buys what—bound to be a pound or so to be got out of it. By the way, Tom, I've had something on my mind most of the day. Let's go back out to the kitchens—the crowd is thinning out considerably now.'

There was a maze of rooms at the rear and it took Willy some while to find the right one.

'It's in here. Yes, this is the room. Yes, look there, Tom. Can you see anything?' He pointed to a modern white-painted kitchen dresser, with open shelves and cupboards underneath—Lot 830 in the catalogue.

'I don't follow you. All I can see is a modern painted dresser. What's the idea?'

'What's so special about the dresser? I've been worrying about it all the afternoon.'

'Why, Willy?'

'Do you remember the first time we came in here? The two Tiddingtons were hanging around.'

'That's right—I remember now. Young Tiddy was stood up on

the bottom part of that dresser—likes to make an exhibition of himself.'

'He was having a good look at the shelves. Now why on earth should he have been doing that?'

'Perhaps he's thinking of buying it for his own home.'

'Not on your life, Tom. Look, there's no one about. They may have something hidden up there on the top of the dresser. I'm going up to see. . . . Oh ho! What on earth . . . ?'

'Anything up there?'

'Sure is, Tom, but I can't make it out—just a bundle of tatty old umbrellas and walking-sticks. Lot 852 on the ticket here. Oh, so that's it, is it? I say, look at this—but make sure there's no one about.'

Tom poked his head round the door. 'Hurry up if you're going to! —there are two people down the corridor talking to a porter.'

Willy jerked a walking-stick out of the bundle, jumped down from the dresser, and handed it to Tom. 'What do you make of that?'

Tom whistled, and gave a careful scrutiny to the 'Dandy's' walking-stick he was holding. It had been made in France, about 1820. Its heavy, beautifully decorated knob was undoubtedly solid gold.

'That's gold or I'm a Dutchman—good twelve ounces there and looks like twenty-two carat.'

Willy was back on the dresser in no time, jamming the walking-stick down in amongst the others, this time knob first so that it was completely hidden.

Tom was checking the catalogue. ' "Lot 852. Bundle of sundry walking-sticks and umbrellas, some a/f." Looks as if that one has slipped by all right. I suppose the Tiddingtons spotted it and shifted the whole lot up on top of the dresser—not the kind of lot to be missed and, if it was, not important enough for anyone to bother with unduly.'

'I wonder how many more know it is up there?'

'Perhaps the porter does.'

'Shouldn't think so, Tom. If any of the porters had a hand in it they would have removed it from the bundle and hidden it away until after the sale—not left it in the lot.'

'Be a good idea to claim it before the sale starts. The old man Tiddington doesn't give anything away if he can help it. Better stake our claim.'

'Let's get cracking. I've had enough for one day, and it will be worse tomorrow.'

On the way out they bumped into Fred Mellis and a small crowd of other dealers.

Willy did a lot of business with Fred, whom he numbered amongst his best trade customers.

'Hallo, Fred—George.'

'Hallo, Willy. Hallo, Tom. Going home with your pockets well filled?'

'Yes. Got all the Battersea enamel boxes up my jumper. What do you think of it, Fred?'

'Some good stuff here, boy. Can't say what we'll do tomorrow though—probably be able to buy a few lots. There is going to be some fun and games by the look of things. You know who has "viewed", of course?'

'I heard Goldensky has been down.'

'Not only Goldensky but Toiple and old Hagar himself.'

'No!' Both Willy and Tom whistled.

Toiple and Hagar were all right. They never bid against the smaller dealers and never left prices on the book. Firmly believing that the boys had to live, they waited until the very last and final round of the settlement, claimed and bid for what they wanted, and then settled the lot between themselves going back by train or in their car.

Toiple was a very rich man and a top-rate dealer. Hagar was reputed to be a millionaire and was one of the finest judges of antique furniture in the world. He was a collector in the loose sense of the word, selling what he did not wish to keep and making it pay for what he did—in reality a dealer. He had a wonderful clientele amongst his friends, especially in America, and never found it necessary to have a shop.

'That means a real good scrap—serve Goldensky right. He'll either get nothing or else a good hammering.'

'I pity any private buyer who fancies his chances and gets up against either of those two. Once old Hagar gets the bit between his teeth there's no stopping him. He will never let go of a lot against a private buyer until it reaches about four times what it is really worth. Quite right too.'

'One thing about the old man is that if he ever gets the lot dropped on him he can always park it on to one of his friends, and anyway a loss of a thousand or two is nothing to him.'

'You off now, Willy? Tom?'

'Yes. Goodbye, all. Hope you get punctures all the way tomorrow.'

'Old Hagar himself, eh?' remarked Tom on the way home. 'What has brought him down? Good stuff there, yes, but most of it not good enough for him.'

'I think he wants something in one of the corridors.'

5 The Reuthen House sale

The first day of the Reuthen House sale was one of those glorious June mornings which promised to become a real scorcher by the afternoon. A huge marquee had been erected on the lawn in front of the main drawing-room. Things were to be conducted à la London style, the selling taking place in the marquee with all the transportable lots being brought in through a special entrance just by the auctioneer's rostrum and taken back into the house as soon as they were sold; once the sale started no one would be allowed into the house on any pretext, and things that were too heavy to be moved would stay where they were, which suited Tom and Willy very well—their thoughts were on the English Colonial side-table in the badly lit corridor.

'Look, Willy,' said Tom, 'there's Gaveeney. You want to put him wise about that font, don't you? If Peter gets hold of him there'll be a nasty stink.'

Willy sauntered over to where Gaveeney was standing alternately stroking his nose and thumbing over the catalogue. He took a swipe at a pestering fly, annoyance on his pudgy face. Gaveeney, who was fifty-five and weighed fifteen stone, was already feeling the heat.

'Some good stuff here, sir.'

'Not bad, Shaun. I've seen better, but there will be some pickings no doubt, despite the fact that our old arch-enemy Goldensky viewed this sale and has no doubt left some pretty heavy commission with the auctioneer. Pity he won't come into the ring—wastes a lot of money.'

'By the way, sir, can I just explain something?'

Willy told the tale of the font. Gaveeney roared with laughter. That was what he called a real joke.

'Good for you, Shaun! It's a pleasure to hear of someone using his brains like that. Far too many of these men hanging round for the crumbs. If he says anything to me I'll say I left the matter entirely to you and have no more interest in the font now that the whole of the trade knows what it cost. Now look, Shaun, you have given me some useful information in the past, so here's a tip. "Lot 130—pair of Chelsea Tureens with lids, in the shape of cabbages. Yellow-and-green decoration." In fact they're Longton Hall. I am not the only one who knows, otherwise I would not be telling you. The ring will buy them—I've blasted Goldensky off them. You can stand in up to six hundred pounds for the pair, you won't hold them. I want half your share of knockout money on that lot, and keep your mouth shut.'

'It's a bit awkward, sir. Tom Elliot and I have agreed to go in double-handed. Can he come in?'

'Yes, the same will apply to him. Half share and keep his mouth shut.'

'I will answer for him, sir. Thanks very much.'

The fact that he often denounced other dealers for 'plugging' did not prevent Willy from being a 'plug' himself. That was different.

Ninety-eight dealers all told—some good, some bad, and others just plain dishonest. The bidding had begun in the marquee, where faces were already being mopped with handkerchiefs. The sun was blazing down and it was like an oven inside.

'How's it goin' in there, Ropey?' asked Willy as the dealer emerged, shirt-sleeved and sweating.

'Oh, O.K., I guess. Haltain's doing the buying for the London boys. The big stuff isn't coming up yet but Toiple is around somewhere. Reg Bardon is in there looking after the smaller stuff and Fred Mellis is taking over from him. I've got a message for you, Shaun. You take over from Fred before lunch, at about twelve-thirty.'

'Who said so?' asked Willy.

'Heberman said so. He's managing the settlement.'

This was a leg-up for Willy—his first appointment as a 'watchdog'. Somebody's got something to do with this, he said to himself. Twelve-thirty, eh? Sixty lots an hour being sold, with luck. Be somewhere in the region of Lot 120 then. Lot 130 is the pair of cabbages. Good old Gaveeney!

As each lot was sold the price and the buyer were carefully noted by the watchdogs. It was not their job to oppose the bidding of a fellow dealer, unless that dealer was in opposition to the ring, but to take up the bidding against any private buyer who might have beaten that previous dealer. The name of any dealer giving up the bidding was noted down to exclude him from the settlement on that particular lot.

If the opposition proved too strong for the local watchdog then the London man took over. If it looked like being too strong even for him the really heavy guns, who were never far away, were called up.

At no time was there a chance for a private buyer to bid for a really good antique without having the entire weight of the ring against him. Those lots which were bought privately against the trade either had something wrong with them or were priced very hot.

This sale was fast and furious. Time and time again private buyers had a good go at one another, bidding recklessly and without reference to the real value of the stuff. The prices soared beyond all reason with the grim determination of the contestants not to be out-bid, the loser having at least the savage satisfaction that the winner had paid through the nose for his triumph.

'I want a private word with you,' Willy whispered to young Tiddington, taking advantage of a lull in the proceedings. 'Come out for a second, will you?'

Out on the lawn, under a huge copper beech, he went on: 'It's about those walking-sticks on top of the dresser.'

Tiddy swore. He'd spent upwards of half an hour standing in the corner of the room with the bundle of sticks and umbrellas hidden behind him, waiting for the room to empty so that he could climb up and stow the lot away on top of the dresser. Then Shaun and Elliot had had to come in and spot him up there!

'O.K., Shaun,' he sighed, mopping his face. 'Father and I thought we had that one to ourselves. Anyone else seen it?'

'Not that I know of. *You'd* better buy it, of course—second-hand walking-sticks are more in your line than mine. Everyone'd smell a rat if Tom or I bid for it. But no sneaking off with it, mind, or I'll see you never get into a settlement again.'

Tiddy junior went off to break the bad tidings to his father.

As a matter of fact the Tiddingtons had a bargain in the stick. Two days later they bought it under the hammer for twenty-eight shillings; and after paying out Shaun and Elliot thirteen pounds each, during a private settlement between the four of them, they sold the walking-stick almost at once to another dealer for seventy-five pounds. A close examination revealed a hall-mark, placed at random in the ornamentation, done in the usual French manner. The weight proved to be just over seven ounces.

The owners did not know the walking-stick existed, so it was no loss to them. It had been up in the attics for nearly a century and had escaped four successive inventories over the years.

Willy was back in the marquee in time for Lot 121 to come up.

' "A very fine pair of English eighteenth-century mahogany arm-chairs of the Chippendale period." We believe, ladies and gentlemen, that the backs are upholstered in the original petit-point material.' Slowly the auctioneer enunciated every word; this was an important lot.

Willy looked across at Haltain, the London dealer, who was still there buying.

'Who'll put me in, please?' from the rostrum.

'Fifty pounds!' cried a private bidder from the middle of the tent. She must have wished the ground would open and swallow her as the auctioneer cut in with his own bid:

'Five hundred pounds bid.'

He obviously had a good price left with him—Goldensky for certain.

'Thank you, sir, five hundred and twenty-five bid, five hundred and twenty-five pounds.' A private bid from the side of the marquee—wealthy looking 'herb'.

At six hundred pounds the private 'herb' was finished and the bidding was with the auctioneer. Haltain held back to make sure no more private buyers were likely to interfere. The auctioneer was preparing to bring down his hammer.

'Any more bids? I am selling this wonderful pair of chairs for the sum of six hundred pounds. Have you all finished?'

Haltain waved his catalogue.

'Six hundred and twenty-five!' and so it went on. At nine hundred pounds Haltain glanced behind him. The bidding was getting near his limit. He reckoned one thousand pounds for the pair. Sure enough, there was Toiple down at the bottom of the marquee with Hagar behind him. Toiple threaded his way up and stood behind Haltain. He had no wish to enter the bidding, but stood with his hand on Haltain's shoulder. While the hand remained there, the bidding would go on. At one thousand, two hundred and twenty-five pounds the hand was withdrawn. The chairs were declared sold but the buyer was not named. Goldensky had them.

Hagar smiled thinly. Before this time tomorrow the glad tidings would be spread around that Goldensky had burnt his fingers on the purchase of a pair of Chippendale armchairs.

' "Lot 130. A pair of Chelsea tureens with lids",' etc., etc.

Tom, who had taken up a position in the middle of the marquee, at this moment shouted out in a loud voice: 'Excuse me, sir, but they are Samson of Paris, aren't they?'

This dodge was as old as the hills but seldom failed to work. The auctioneer glared at Tom. He was not used to this kind of interruption.

'This lot is being sold in accordance with the conditions as laid down in the catalogue.' He had no intention of entering into a discussion. They had been catalogued as Chelsea and if mis-described—well, that was just too bad. It was no responsibility of the auctioneer's. He himself did not know whether they were Chelsea, Samson, or Sweet Fanny Adams.

Most collectors of porcelain know about Samson of Paris, a nineteenth-century wizard who was responsible for more porcelain fakes than any other individual.

Three private people had made up their minds to make a serious attempt to buy these two cabbages. After Tom's query two, who lacked specialized knowledge on Chelsea, became faint-hearted. 'Be foolish to give a lot of money for wrong stuff—better wait and see who bids.' Both had lost interest with their courage. The third one was still undecided. He could well have afforded to push the ring out of the bidding, but there was no point in wasting money. Samson, eh? He was unconvinced and still interested—and yet when he had examined the tureens they had not seemed quite 'Chelsea' somehow. He would watch the dealers and the bidding.

'Who will put me in?'

'Fifty bob!' from Willy at the back.

'Come, come, I expect a better start than that.'

'It's a bid, sir, and you haven't had a better one.'

That finished off the third interested private purchaser. The auctioneer decided to accept the bid.

'Fifty shillings bid. Any advance on fifty. Fifty-five. Fifty-five. Sixty. Sixty-five. Sixty-five. Seventy . . .'

After a short skirmish with a good-looking woman in a pink dress too tight round the hips and too low in front, Willy was in possession of the cabbages for nine pounds ten shillings—thanks to Tom and Gaveeney, the latter somehow or other having persuaded Goldensky to relinquish interest in them.

At one o'clock the sale was halted for a luncheon break of half an hour. Breathing fresh air again, people realized what a fug there had been in the marquee. The lawns and park were already dotted with picnicking groups, some with cloths spread with salads and cold chicken, others more modest with sandwiches and thermos flasks. There was a mobile canteen near the front porch, and there was a rush on ice-creams and lemonade. The wise ones got in their cars and slipped down to the Bull, two and a half miles from Reuthen House.

Of the one hundred and forty lots already sold the 'boys' were in possession of nine major and twenty minor ones. The best stuff in the whole sale was coming up in the afternoon.

A breeze had sprung up, and the marquee was more bearable when the sale began again punctually at 1.30 p.m. Apart from one interruption, when an elderly man went off in a dead faint and the porters rushed out and in with glasses of water, the items were sold smoothly and the bidding was still very spirited, even fantastic. The day's selling finished at half past four with three hundred lots sold—an average of fifty-four an hour —good going considering the heat.

Private opposition had been more pronounced in the afternoon. Not on the finest pieces, which were right out of the average punter's appreciation and reckoning, but on the good medium stuff—chests of drawers, toilet mirrors, and suchlike. This was upsetting to the smaller dealers who were not prepared to risk small fortunes on the best afterwards in the settlement—on goods which they did not properly understand. Not many of the lesser items had been purchased for the boys in the afternoon —things which should have gone for about twelve pounds ten to fifteen pounds apiece had been run up and battled over, private bid against private bid, to thirty pounds and sometimes over forty.

As for small tiddly lots—the private people went plain barmy. A good many had come to the sale with a five-pound note to spend, and it seemed not to matter what they got for it as long as it was 'something from Reuthen House'.

Goldensky, by not being in the settlement, and by leaving prices with the auctioneer which were too high for the smaller dealers, had spoilt the sale for the ring, local dealers and Londoners alike; and the auctioneer had other commissions on his book. But, nevertheless, the boys had cleared eighteen important lots and thirty-one smaller ones, not counting the three lots purchased by Toiple during the afternoon and the two which Hagar himself bought. These last five had been got against Goldensky and were all in the 'thousand' category; it was unlikely that anyone would lay any claim for a settlement on them.

Lot 227, the American side-table, had been bought for one hundred and forty pounds; Goldensky, having too much to look at and reckon up by the way of the fine pieces, had had no time or inclination to nose round looking for 'chancy' lots. He missed it completely.

Willy and Tom had a little conference before setting out for Abberton, where the settlement was to be held at the Royal George Hotel.

'Haltain bought the side-table. Haven't heard a word, of course, Tom, but I'm certain that's the lot which brought Hagar down here. Toiple could have handled the rest. What are we going to do? Trust to luck and have a real good bash at it?'

'How much do you think it would fetch if we get landed with it?'

'Oh, I guess five hundred certain. Any Yankee dealer would give that much for it. Furniture of the "Colonial" period fetches real money in the States.'

'What about three-to-one odds? It's a fair gamble.'

'Crumbs, Willy! D'ye mean fifteen hundred pounds?'

Willy nodded. According to his calculation, if they ducked out of the bidding at one thousand four hundred and fifty pounds they would not hold the table against the top London boys. If by ill chance they did, it would be seven hundred and twenty-five each to stump up.

'Aye, let's give them a surprise. I've got enough cash on me to cover it. Mark you, Tom, don't get faint-hearted in the middle of it. The London crowd will try all sorts of dodges to put us off.'

Tom agreed, with a certain amount of hesitation. Seven hundred and twenty-five to pay out with a loss of anything up to five hundred would not break him by any means, but he hated losing hard-earned money. Willy would know what he was up to, though.

'Look, Tom—remember, now. It's no good standing next to one another when that lot comes up. Stand somewhere opposite and when the bidding gets to one thousand two hundred and fifty on top of the buying price, you duck and go out. I'll do the same if it is nearest me. I'm fairly certain, though, that Hagar will end up with it, and probably over two thousand at that.'

Off they went to Abberton, a small town six miles away, to gamble the biggest amount either had ever placed on a single piece of furniture.

There were ninety-four of the 'boys' present in the huge bare room used for receptions, with its stale, unused smell of spirits and tobacco. Heberman was in the chair; he was detested by most small country dealers, for he nearly always named them out of the first round. Being 'named out' meant that one was not considered of sufficient standing to go into the second round of the knockout; London dealers were never named out; it was always the small country dealers and the odds and sods. For all their resentment, however, they had to admit that Heberman was scrupulously fair and wouldn't stand any nonsense or arguments; so after a long history of factious dispute he was now generally acknowledged the 'king' of the knockout all over the country.

Today thirty of the ninety-four were named out, which meant that they, against the rest, were required, collectively or singly, to advance the bidding on each lot as it was called by as much as they reckoned it was worth, or dared to run it up against the big boys. The total amount so advanced in this round—four hundred and ten pounds—was paid out by the highest bidders, who were left to carry their items into the next round, and divided among the ninety-four dealers present. The first-rounders were paid their share and were asked to leave the room before the next round began.

On this occasion what is called a 'general settlement' was to take place. This meant that round one was concluded on all the lots, including the Yankee table and the cabbages, before round two began, and so on. In this way the lesser men were knocked out before the final rounds and the really big men made their final settlements on all the lots in privacy.

The dealers remaining for the second round were all credited with their share, and new lists were made for the next tussle.

During the commotion caused by the departure of the small-timers, Willy went casually up to Heberman.

'I'm holding the cabbages, as you know. Both Elliot and I reckon them real money. Pity to make us bid in the next round. It will only mean a lot of money to be divided amongst more than necessary.'

'I know all about that, Shaun. You were only allowed to buy them under the hammer to throw everybody out of step on them. If any of the big boys here had bought them at the sale, every Tom, Dick, and Harry would be claiming them. As it is most of them, particularly the furniture wallahs, haven't a clue as to their value. In the second round you will have to hold them against all comers, other than the London boys and anyone else who looks like reckoning them and who will get the tip-off to stop bidding.'

'Ah, that's just what I wanted to know, Mr Heberman. Oh, and by the way, we also reckon Lot 227 at a good figure and then some more on the top of that.'

Heberman's eyes narrowed.

'Who's using you as a plug on that lot?'

'No one. Tom spotted it and we worked it out together. I've got a special reference-book which covers that sort of furniture. Does the same apply on that lot or do we have to wreck it for the London boys?'

Heberman did not answer immediately. As Chairman, he was not required to bid on any lot, but went right through to the last of the settling. His share of the proceeds was always high, even if his knowledge did not entitle him to that amount. Most of the big noises used him to work little schemes for their own particular benefit. Gaveeney had told him about the Longton Hall cabbages and he would, no doubt, receive a dab in the hand from Gaveeney if things went favourably for the latter. His main and most important job was to weed out the dealers according to their strength, so that when the big money was being put on, the fewest number possible were left to share it. If Shaun and Elliot had somehow 'got on' to the American side-table—the most important lot in the entire sale—it would not do to have them bidding big money in the second round which would be divided out between sixty-four dealers. His action in letting two country dealers into the third and possibly the fourth round would need some explaining to the big noises. However, it was by far the best money-saving policy, and after all, that was the main consideration.

He nodded reluctantly at Shaun. 'The same will apply to that.' Then he cleared his throat. 'All right, gentlemen! We will now have a division —London versus Country. Will all country dealers stay on the left side of the room and will all London move over to the right?'

There was a general scuffle and postman's knock as sixty-one dealers, not counting the three officiating at the table, sorted themselves out. The London dealers were still in the minority.

Again Heberman called the catalogue and this time the bidding was much more spirited. Here were men who knew how to appraise the value of antiques and were not afraid to bid according to their knowledge. One or two of the very fine pieces were not claimed. They had cost a great deal of money under the hammer, and no country dealer had either sufficient pluck or knowledge to bid them up to a higher figure. No doubt some of the London boys would have a go at them later on, and finally the issue would be decided by perhaps two or three, plus Toiple and Hagar.

Fred Mellis was in fine form, forcing the price skyhigh on some items. He managed to hold six good intermediate lots, including a fine Sheraton-period concave-fronted enclosed make-up table with three separate tambour slides—an unusual piece, and he had a customer for it. This cost him one hundred and thirty-nine pounds, fifty-two at the auction and eighty-seven put on in the settlement. He had a hot lot dropped on him by way of a mediocre Gothic-style Chippendale Gainsborough-type armchair for one hundred and five pounds—cost thirty-two under the hammer.

The London boys by no means had it all their own way. Willy's cabbages were called and two hundred pounds slammed on them by a dealer from the Midlands. This was regrettable in one way, as the majority of the country dealers, and also some of the London ones, knew nothing about the cabbages and were quite prepared to accept them as Samson of Paris as Tom had suggested. As it was they would get their share of the big money, benefiting by the Midland dealer's knowledge and the risk he took.

The cabbages were held into the third round for two hundred on.

The Yankee table came in for a rousing six-hundred-and-ten-pounds advance from Fred Mellis, who was bidding for a three-handed syndicate on that particular piece of furniture. Willy and Tom abstained from bidding and it was held by London into the third round for seven hundred and fifty pounds. That is to say, it had been bought under the hammer for one hundred and forty pounds and advanced in the settlement by six hundred and ten pounds.

A real good hot-under-the-collar time was had by all, some one thousand and sixteen pounds having been advanced by the second-rounders.

Calculations were fast and head-scratching went on up there on the table as those who were now holding the various items were called upon to pay the amounts they had advanced.

Before the beginning of the third round one of the two men who had been helping Heberman was paid off and left. Matters would now become hush-hush and very private.

After the exodus of the country dealers the real business started. There were now twenty one London dealers including Heberman and Wenden, who was helping at the table, but not counting Hagar or Toiple, who were lounging somewhere in a private bar. Heberman had little authority now but still kept control of the situation.

'Be a good idea to settle the cabbages and get rid of these three?' indicating the Midlands dealer, Willy, and Tom. There was general assent; the gambling and the dropping of hot lots on to someone else was about to start. Dealer after dealer was knocked out of the diminishing circle until there were only eight very determined dealers left for what looked like being the last but one go.

Round and round the bidding went until Willy ducked out at five hundred and ninety pounds on, faithfully in accordance with his agreement with Gaveeney. There had already been some nasty remarks about people who used plugs but Willy had rounded on the culprit.

'Elliot and I are in two-handed on these. We both know what they are and we have our own ideas about their value. We will bid to that figure, without asking your permission. You mind your own business and we'll be minding ours. Londoners aren't the only people with knowledge—and there's another lot yet we're claiming.'

'All right, you two, cut the cackle, there's twenty-one pounds apiece for you and Elliot out of this round, making thirty-three each. Seven fivers—give me two pound change, will you?'

Willy handed back three pounds. So did Tom. Heberman's assistant acknowledged the extra pound by lifting the corner of his mouth for what was intended as a smile. These two boys weren't bad 'uns—particularly Shaun—crafty devil—could rely on him, though. Somebody was obviously 'plugging' him into the cabbages, but he had given no clue by word or look.

Willy and Tom were well satisfied. By rights they were not entitled to any money at all. Neither of them would have risked six hundred pounds on the cabbages without Gaveeney's backing. Thirty-three pounds would be going to him, but they still had fifteen pounds ten shillings each.

The circle was now re-forming for the piece of American furniture. The cabbages would be settled after Shaun, Elliot, and the obstinate Midlands dealer had been finally winkled out.

Willy winked across at Tom. They had, after a bit of jostling, got opposite each other, as prearranged. It was Tom's turn to start the ball rolling.

'Don't let's waste time,' someone said. 'Tenners?'

'Six hundred and twenty,' from Tom, and so it started.

When it came round to the Midlands dealer, at six hundred and ninety pounds on, he declined to bid. He was more of a porcelain buyer and knew nothing about this piece of furniture; he had stayed in just long enough to earn himself three pounds without making any bid.

He was sarcastically told that it had hardly been worth while putting himself in, was paid out, and told to go.

When the total price was ten pounds short of a thousand, six dealers went out and were paid their share.

The bidding started again between the fourteen dealers. They were all good men, and all out for a gamble. Gaveeney was still in—more for the fun of it than anything else. He knew the piece was worth money, real money, but he did not intend to stay in much longer. The cabbages still had to be settled and he wanted to hold them away from his colleagues if he could.

The bidding came round to Tom at one thousand, three hundred and ten pounds on and Tom ducked. 'That's enough for me. I'm out.'

He was paid forty-one pounds, and as he left the room he was surprised by a broad wink from Willy. What was up? Was Willy going to stay in for another go? They had agreed to come out at the nearest figure to a total of fifteen hundred.

Willy's calculation had been quick. Tom was opposite to him. There were six more bids to go before he was forced to bid. That meant another sixty pounds to be put on before his turn came. When the bidding did get round to him, he declined and 'went out'.

'You cunning devil, Shaun,' said Heberman. 'You've got the better of your pal by four quid.'

'Just a matter of luck, sir. The bidding happened to come round that way. Could easily have been me that had to go first.'

'Here's your money, Shaun. Forty-five pounds. You deserve it for your cheek.'

Willy walked casually from the room where, for the first time in his

E

life, he had been in the fifth round of an important sale settlement.

Willy found Tom in the saloon bar, together with over a dozen more dealers.

'Get us a drink, Tom. I'm devilish thirsty after that lot.'

'You been double-crossing me, Willy?'

'No, just used my head—earned another four quid by staying in the bidding until it got to my turn to bid. Don't forget they were bidding up in tenners. It was worth waiting for.'

Tom immediately claimed half share. Willy refused, and after a fair amount of light-hearted abuse was forced into buying a round of drinks that cost him over four pounds. He was happy enough not to care. He was taking home eighty-nine pounds, not counting the sixteen pounds he would be paying back to Gaveeney later on. Not a bad day at all, considering.

'Thank goodness that's over,' said Tom when they got outside. 'I'll never risk that much money again on something I'd have a job to sell if I got landed with it. I lost two pounds in sweat back there in that room during the last round.'

They both went home well satisfied.

The owners were also pleased at the prices they had got, some of them well over the thousand-pound mark. They would not have been quite so pleased had they been aware of what was going on in the reception-room of the Royal George in Abberton, where, once the really big men got down to business, some eight thousand five hundred pounds changed hands in the last rounds on the fine pieces.

The trade had what could be called a reasonably fair day.

The auctioneer was well pleased with the day's sale. Goldensky's opposition to his fellow dealers had been responsible for some very good prices, and the wildly erratic bidding from some of the private purchasers had swelled the day's total to a figure beyond expectation. He viewed the 'antique traders' with mixed feelings. He knew there had been a strong ring at work and without his having received Goldensky's commissions the ring would have had things all its own way. On the other hand, had no dealers attended the sale the finest things would have fetched hardly any price at all. He knew, of course, that a settlement was taking place at the George, but that was none of his business.

But there *were* one or two discontented people, among them a young lady who was getting married shortly and had come over to the sale with her grandfather in the hopes of acquiring one or two pieces of furniture.

'Those wretched dealers, Grandad—they just don't give anyone a chance! I really wanted that little Sheraton side-table, but how could I possibly buy it against that pack of greedy wolves? John will be *furious* when he finds out how much they made me pay for the Chippendale chest of drawers. It isn't fair.'

'You paid too much for that, my dear. Don't be in such a hurry. One day you will have most of my furniture anyway. This is the best advice I can give you: don't buy much at auction sales. Unless you know enough you may buy a genuine piece at a wrong price. You can also buy the wrong article at the wrong price, which is far worse. I gave a lot of money once at an auction for a pair of walnut stools—oh yes, I knew all about them, or thought I did. I beat all the dealers on them. As it turned out, the person against whom I was actually bidding was a man who knew just about as much as I did about them. They cost me two hundred pounds then, and that was a long time ago. Had I ever been able to bring myself to sell them, I could never have got more than twenty pounds. They're both duds. Don't be tempted by a bargain, either. There is always something wrong with it or the person who is selling it. I've dealt with Cummington for years. I know he's a bit old-fashioned—hasn't got the kind of shop that's popular these days—but he's got sound knowledge and as far as I know has never had dealings in the ring. He very seldom has anything approaching a bargain, at any rate not an intentional one; but to my certain knowledge he has never diddled anyone in his life. Going into his shop may not be as exciting as going to a sale, but it is much safer. I have done a lot of business with that man in the past. On some of the things he bought from me I know he made fifty per cent and more, but I suppose he deserved it. I never begrudge a good man a good profit. There, my dear—a lecture from your grandfather. And here's a little present from him too. In days to come when you look at your chest of drawers, filled perhaps with your children's clothes or toys, you can say to yourself. "Grandad bought it for me but I made him pay too much money for it." '

'That's very sweet of you, Grandpa. John will be delighted as well, but what I can't stand are all these terrible dealers who form themselves into a ring or something. I don't understand what they do. A friend of mine was trying to explain it to me.'

'They have to live, my dear. . . . Who can blame them? If anyone puts anything into a sale it is only for one of two reasons, or both—either to get rid of something they don't want, or to sell something for as much as they can get for it. If it's something they don't want anyway, whatever it fetches will leave them content. If it is sold to make money, then it is up to the owner to protect his goods against those who may be sharper-witted or more knowledgeable. Of course, if you like to gamble on something fetching a good price—perhaps even more than its proper price—at a sale, there's nothing to stop you. But you've no cause to wail or grumble if you're outsmarted by this so-called ring. I am a firm believer in selling direct to a good antique dealer—like old Cummington. You may not get so much from him as you would from a sale where there was strong opposition, but taking carriage, auctioneers' commission, and other expenses into consideration, you do better with him in the long run. If the dealer wants to do more business with you, he will be honest enough, providing you have the sense to realize that he has his expenses and overheads and has got to make a profit. If you try to make him pay a price which leaves him no margin, he will soon sum you up and ultimately get the better of you.'

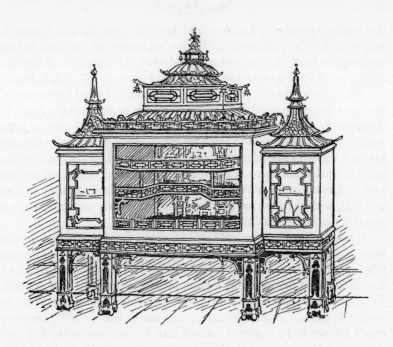

6   *Opportunity Knocks But Once*

'Do you feel any better now, dear?'

It was 8.30 a.m. and Willy had just woken up from a doze when his wife spoke. Normally he would have been up and dressed long before, but he had had a shocking night—just one continual trot. He blamed it on the pork pies he had eaten last night after a long day at a sale, with no time for a proper meal.

Ethel was quite anxious about her husband; she had never seen him look so rough. My, he did look bad! His face was a sickly greenish-white tinge—eyes hollowed and cheeks pinched in.

The thought of being made to stay in bed all day was enough for Willy.

'I'll feel better when I'm up.' He doubted if he would, but anything to get out of being fussed over. He would have been furious if his wife had made no attempt to fuss over him, but seeing that she *was* fussing, it was up to him to pooh-pooh it. He got up, aching all over and feeling as though a herd of cows had trampled over his stomach in the night. After a good douche under the cold tap and a shave he felt slightly better.

What was he going to do all day? There was that load of furniture he'd sold to a dealer up north. He ought to take it to the carrier's depot in Torminster. The thought of loading six pieces of furniture, one of them a heavy dining table, was too much for him ... then, as he slowly adjusted his tie, a sudden inspiration came—an inspiration which crowded out his aches and pains and opened up a reserve store of energy. He took another look at himself in the mirror—face white and washed out, eyes sunken and dull, with deep purple bags under them—it was certainly worth a try. If it did not succeed nothing else would.

It was Jo Busting who had told him about the china-cabinet. Jo had been to some obscure farmhouse sale with Reg Bardon, who had known nothing about the sale till Jo tipped him off that it was worth going to. And if it hadn't been for Reg's mean behaviour to Jo on that occasion Jo would never have told Willy about the cabinet. How important an event this tenuous chain of circumstances was to lead to Willy certainly didn't foresee as he buttoned himself into an overcoat in the hall and suppressed a queasy turn in his stomach at the sight of the first of the November leaves whirling and scuttering down the path.

Jo was a real hanger-on, never after goods, only money, and his idea in tipping Reg off about the sale was that he might get a lift there and back and a chance to get a pound or two off him in knockout money. But Reg had not only done him down over the money but left him stranded a mile outside the village: 'Sorry, Jo—these two chairs've got to go on the front seat. As you can see there isn't an inch to spare. Certain to be a bus from Tuderwell.'

But there wasn't; and after half an hour or more of pacing up and down the small main street, trying in vain for a lift, he had worked himself up into a frenzy about Reg Bardon. Thus obsessed he'd passed and re-passed a cottage window for the fourth time before something made him pull up with a jolt. He had a quick look through the window: there, taking up most of the far wall in the tiny room, was a gilt cabinet, most delicately carved. Jo's knowledge was limited, but his instinct told him he was on to a 'good lot'.

'Never seen anything like it before. I wonder if ...' At that moment his view of the cabinet was obscured by a pair of hostile eyes in an angry wrinkled face framed in wisps of grey hair. The next moment he was looking at a drawn blind.

This might be big stuff—whom should he tip off about it? A certain pleasant unfamiliar sense of power warmed him on his journey into the nearest market town in a friend's lorry. And there, in a pub, he chanced to meet Willy on his way back from a sale in Tormouth. Willy was amiable enough, and gave him a lift the rest of the way home. But he didn't tell Willy then; there was something off-putting about Shaun's beaky face and dark penetrating eyes that missed so little, his firm rather thin lips that gave away nothing, and about his abrupt straight-to-the-point way of dealing; everyone said he was on the up-and-up—must be salting away quite a packet—all the more reason for him to let up a bit. By this Jo meant let *out* a bit; living as he did so largely upon the results of rumour and pub gossip, Jo preferred a man to be loose-mouthed, easy-come-easy-go. Whereas Shaun had stuck to his early maxim—live and let live and the Devil take the hindmost; and there was no guessing what went on underneath that shock of dark hair, as thick as ever, though greying a little at the sides. But as it happened Willy *did* put a bit of business Jo's way, and unknowingly did himself a good turn as well. Having no one better to trust, he left some prices with him to buy some lots in one of the local sale-rooms.

'Got to be in Tormouth again early tomorrow,' he explained, reaching across to open the car door.

Jo was delighted to have someone else's prices, and made himself four pounds in the settlement, putting in Willy as an absentee and making use of Willy's prices to increase the knockout money due to himself. Jo held one lot—a small Sheraton-period mahogany revolving-top music-stool—settled the account and took the stool to his own house where Shaun picked it up on his way back from Tormouth.

'Thanks for bringing the stool round here for me,' Willy said after pocketing his share of the knockout money and giving Jo a pound note. 'I'm very pleased with it. Don't often find them with square taper legs and spade feet—nearly always heavy round-turned legs.'

Jo pocketed his extra pound. Queer chap, Shaun, he thought. Never really done me a bad, except that one time he handed me a hot lot. Can't fathom him. 'The cat who walks by himself' would fit. Never stingy with the money. Might do worse than tell Shaun about that cabinet—one in the eye for Bardon if it turns out to be good—make him sorry he let me down so badly yesterday.

'Oh, by the way, Willy, how do I stand if I put you on to a good lot?'
Willy pricked up his ears. Jo Busting got around a bit.

'Mind you, I don't know just how good it is. I've never seen anything
like it in all my life. Over in a cottage a few yards away from the Wink
and Garter in Tuderwell.'

Jo spread himself a bit on the details and Willy made a mental note to
visit Reg Bardon in the morning to see what he had bought at that
farmhouse sale. He listened attentively to Jo's story. He knew Tuderwell
—often went through the village but had never called at the Wink and
Garter.

'Well, it's there all right, but I doubt if you'll be able to get past that
old woman. Proper vixen she looked to me. How do I stand if it's any
good and you get it?'

'Look, Jo, I can't tell you. It may be a wash-out, it may be a thunder-
ing good lot—can't say until I set eyes on it. If I get it and buy it right,
you will be on to a proper share—fiver—tenner—twenty, who knows?'

With that Jo had to be content. Willy said good night, returning
home in deep thought. If Jo Busting had given him an unexaggerated
and accurate description, residing in Tuderwell was one of the rarest
pieces of English eighteenth-century furniture in England, maybe in the
whole world.

But how to get a look at it? Too much interest might arouse suspicions. The idea of fishing for information at the Wink and Garter was
dismissed—too risky. How to get inside that cottage?

A trip through the village in his car established the location of the
cottage. A further visit that night with a torch established the identity of
the china-cabinet. It had been haunting Willy now for over two weeks. . . .

He had another look in the hall mirror—he certainly looked ill
enough. There was a chance, just a chance, that his plan would come off.

'You up already, dear?' called Ethel from the kitchen. 'I thought you
were going to stay in bed—at least this morning. What's the good of me
trying to look after you if you won't stay in bed? I'm just making you
some arrowroot to settle your stomach.'

'Arrowroot! *Arrowroot?* You don't catch me taking that beastly
slippery muck—make me worse than ever. What I want is a good stiff
brandy and port.'

She came out, wiping her hands on her apron. 'And that's just what
you're not going to have, my lad. The last time you said that, you had it,
and no doubt you can remember the result?'

Willy could, and changed the subject.

'I'm going out now!'

He knew this would make Ethel cross. She dearly loved a chance to mother him, and at the same time boss him about. Slipping out of her clutches would tease her.

'You'll do nothing of the sort, William, after groaning and moaning all through the night. You go in the front room and sit down.'

'I've got to. I'll feel much better when I'm out and about, dear.'

Ethel gave an exasperated sigh. She knew her William. That 'dear' was final. He would go out and nothing short of dropping dead would stop him. Why can't he be like other men? she inwardly sighed as she took down his scarf from its peg. Good safe job, leave at eight in the morning, back at six in the evening, no work Saturdays or Sundays. What a life I have, married to an antique dealer! 'Gone first thing in the morning —not back till dark and nothing to eat all day except trash and bad pork pies. . . . Week in, week out,' she said aloud. Willy had his arm round her waist. He wasn't so ill but that he could appreciate the rounded plumpness of her arm as she raised it. The years had dealt kindly with Ethel; she had filled out but not coarsened.

'Where are you going?' She had a last try. 'I'm sure you could put it off.'

'Not this I can't. It's important and has to be done this morning. I'll be home for lunch, all being well. 'Bye, dear.' A quick peck and he was gone.

Willy parked his car some distance away from the Wink and Garter. He got out and slowly walked back in the direction of the cottage. He passed the pub and, if it hadn't been long before opening time, anyone looking out would have interpreted his gait as a drunken stagger.

He slowed down almost to a crawl, his right hand pressed firmly to the left side of his chest. He gave an extra big stagger—for the benefit of someone looking out of a window on the opposite side of the road. He stopped, his chest heaving as though every breath might be his last. By this time he was outside the cottage. Leaning on the door-jamb he raised his hand with an effort, gave two sharp taps on the iron knocker, and clutched his chest again. Eventually the door was opened and out looked old Grey-hair.

'What do you want?'

The query was sharp. Mrs Kidley always adopted this tone with strangers through force of habit. Brush-sellers, gypsies—thought she'd nothing to do with her time but stand and listen to them.

'Please may I have a glass of water?' A pause. 'I'm not feeling very well.'

This took the old lady aback somewhat. A glass of water was the last thing she had expected to be asked for. She looked closer. In pain. Hand over his heart. Face looks white and drawn.

'Hold on a minute. Hey, Ted! Te-hed! Come out here a minute.'

Ted appeared from the kitchen door at the end of the passage.

'What's up, Ma?'

'Get this gentleman a glass of water. He's not feeling well. Shall I get my daughter-in-law to get the doctor for you, sir?' she suggested grudgingly—proper waste of time it'd be having a doctor—take up her whole morning. But he did look *awful*.

Willy shook his head. 'No thank you, not necessary at all. It's just my heart. I get attacks every now and then. I'm used to them, but this one is severe. I'll be all right in a minute or so. The pain will pass off soon, after I've taken my pills.'

Old Ted appeared with the glass of water. Willy fumbled in his waistcoat pocket for an aspirin which he had put there before leaving home, holding it between finger and thumb as though it were a miracle drug.

'I always carry one of these—just in case. I can never be too careful.' Slowly Willy sipped his water. 'Do you think I could sit down for a minute or two?'

'Cor dang me if we bain't bad-mannered.' Old Ted sounded apologetic. 'Do'ee cum in an' zit down yeer directly,' indicating one of a pair of oak chairs just inside the door. To the left of this was the door leading into the room where the cabinet was.

Two rooms up and two down—the kitchen at the end of this passage. I'm in—now for it!

The two old Kidleys were still regarding him with some alarm.

'Shut the door, Ted—it's draughty for the gentleman and that old nosebag of a Mrs. Wheeler over the road is nearly breaking her blessed neck to see who it is we've got in here.'

Ted shut the door. Willy was well and truly 'in'. His prepared plan ended here, and he must rely on improvisation. Slowly he recovered, accompanied by large noisy exhalations.

'I'm very sorry to have put you to all this inconvenience. I was down here on business and left my car further up in the village. I feel very much better now. Thank you for your hospitality. . . . If you don't mind me saying so, these are a very fine pair of chairs—that and the one I am sitting in. I know something about antiques—hobby of mine.'

A look of pleasure came over old Ted Kidley's face; he had found an ally. His son and daughter-in-law were always on at him and Ma to get rid of this 'old-fashioned junk' and buy something 'modern'. The pair of chairs were two of the worst late-Victorian copies of the Jacobean period Willy had ever seen—a pair of chairs on which some carver had lavished far more time than taste. Ted Kidley, now eighty-three, had bought them second-hand, just before he married sixty-three years ago, for the sum of two shillings the pair.

'Do'ee think zo, zur?'

'Mm. I know a good bit of oak when I see it and this is good oak—fine pair of chairs—have a job to find a better pair—real Jacobean.'

'Thur y'are, Ma. What did I tell 'ee?—doan't want vor tu buy 'em by any chance, do'ee, zurr?'

Ted and his wife were hard up. They had their old-age pensions, but the small savings they had stinted and scraped for all their working lives were now almost gone. They'd lived in the same cottage since they were married. Their son, they told Willy proudly, was earning good money in the nearby brick kilns and had taken a chance to buy their cottage and the one next door for a couple of hundred, so they had a roof over their head. All the same, times were hard, and if the gentleman was thinking of buying the chairs . . .

Willy began to warm up. Things were going his way nicely.

'Buy them? Yes, I should like to buy them very much. I will give you a hundred pounds for the pair.'

He was safe enough in offering this amount, for if he didn't manage to buy the cabinet, or if it turned out not to be what he thought it was, it would be easy enough to say he would be a few days finding the money —give them a false address if they asked—and then disappear never to return.

The Kidleys stared at him with open mouths.

'Hunderd pound?' Ted was the first to recover. 'Hunderd pound and I ony give two bob—ugh!' He broke off as his wife dug her elbow into his stomach. (Trust Ted to make a fool of himself—never would have any sense!—nearly blurted out that he only gave two shillings for them—might put the gentleman off completely—make him change his mind. A hundred pounds!—What won't that buy! See us through our lives in coal. . . .)

'Do you really mean that, sir?' she said.

'Oh yes. I really mean it—if you'll accept the offer, that is. I assure you it *is* a generous offer, but I happen to be very fond of Jacobean oak.'

'Yeou can av 'em, zurr. How be 'ee goin' t'pay for'n?'

'Oh, cash. I always pay cash. Don't believe in cheques. Mind you, I may not have sufficient on me. If I haven't I'll leave a small deposit and return in a day or two to settle up and take the chairs. While I'm here, have you anything else to show me which you think may be of interest?'

As he spoke Willy manœuvred sideways to the door of the front room. 'Do you mind if I look in here?'

'No' for an answer was useless, seeing that Willy had already opened the door and was inside the room. His tongue went dry as his eyes flew to the cabinet standing against the wall. How—he asked himself—how on earth had such a piece of furniture got into a place like this?

He was looking, for the first time outside of a book, at one of the finest and rarest specimens of Chippendale furniture—a giltwood Chinese Chippendale period pagoda china-cabinet.

The centre part had a two-tiered pagoda roof and the two wings had roofs of their own. The overhanging eaves had little bells dangling from them—silver bells, which subsequently proved by their hall-marks to have been made by an English silversmith noted for his silver toys and of worldwide fame for his baby's rattles. The two wings had glazed doors of an intricate pattern and the centre had open shelves whose edges had a gallery with fretting identical to the pattern of the side doors, only in miniature. At the back of each open shelf was a Chinese mirror-painting, a series of landscapes with water and pagodas in the foreground, hills and trees in the background, and a good sprinkling of figures, flowers, and birds. The set of mirrors alone was worth a small fortune.

The cabinet was not on a stand but had pierced and fretted cluster-columned feet about nine inches high. The proportions were superb. It was six feet six inches high and the same in width, and had the appearance of being higher than it actually was.

The cluster columns were repeated on each side, and the centre columns each had a climbing creeper delicately winding its way up—carved by a master. The whole cabinet must be made of pine; no other wood could have been carved in this manner. The gilding was still in first-class condition, although rubbed away to the bare wood in vulnerable spots. Here and there one or two leaves had been broken, but considering the fragility of the entire cabinet, with all the fretting, tracery, individually carved leaves and stalks, and the pierced pagoda tops, it was a miracle for it to be standing there as it was.

Willy brought himself back from another world. It's right, he said to himself, no doubt about that, but what is it doing here in this poky little room? Can it have been planted here by another dealer? No, impossible—besides, the old people were making no attempt to sell it. Look how the woman had behaved when Jo first spotted it. He allowed his gaze to wander round the room . . . slowly . . . slowly. He had a weak feeling at the back of his knees and his stomach, which had caused him so much trouble in the night, started to drag down again.

'Can't see much in here, Mrs—Mrs——? I didn't catch your name?'

'Kidley's th' name. Good old Devonshire name. Bin a Kidley round these yeer parts vor th' last foive 'unerd year an' oi doän zay.'

Old Ted was getting another of his five eggs into the conversation basket. Willy was glad of the opportunity for another covert examination.

'What about the Victorian china-cabinet over there by the wall? My!—what a dust-trap! Still, it has its merits. Friend of mine collects that sort of stuff—can't understand his taste—give me a good old bit of English oak.' (Careful, careful—may have had offers for it.) 'Do you want to sell it?'

The question was casually put and Willy pretended to examine something else in the room. This was the delicate stage, and he did not want to bungle the deal by appearing too eager.

Mrs Kidley looked at her husband. Yes indeed, it was a dust-trap. Time and again she had almost reached the point of selling it but the fact that it had belonged to her grandmother always stopped her.

'Well really, I don't know. I ought not to sell it. It belonged to my grandmother, you see.'

Mrs Kidley spoke much better than her husband. Her grandmother, mother, and she had risen through the scullery and the kitchen to the rank of parlourmaid. Old Ted was a gardener and nothing would ever alter him.

Willy nodded. (Keep her talking. Find out how she came by it. If she's ever had another offer. If so, it's bound to come out in conversation.)

'My daughter-in-law keeps on for me to get rid of it—old-fashioned junk, she calls it. Quite a modern miss, she is—all "contemporary". She told me plain and straight that if I leave it to Bob, that's my son who lives next door, it will go straight into the sale-rooms or on a bonfire, but it has a lot of memories for me.'

Willy nodded again. 'Of course, it must have.'

'My grandmother was in service with Lord Abercoombey, up until the time she was married—started at the house when she was ten. When she got married Lord Abercoombey treated her according to the custom in that family—took her upstairs into the attics where all the unwanted furniture, china, and glass was kept. She was allowed to choose one piece of furniture, one each of china and glass. If she'd been a kitchen-maid, she'd only've had a piece of furniture and china, or in the scullery, just the furniture, and then only if she'd done ten years' service.'

Mrs Kidley settled down to enjoy herself.

'Grandma chose what she thought was the most expensive-looking piece of furniture up there—"all gold it was, standing there looking like a jewel" she used to tell me. And didn't they laugh in the drawing-room when Lord Abercoombey told his wife and some of her friends about it. "Oh no, Algy! Not that horrible old-fashioned piece of Chinese-looking clap-trap? Whatever does she think she is going to do with it? Use it as a birdcage?"

'Grandma treasured it all through her life. I inherited it from her when she died. My mother died when I was born and Grandma brought me up. Doesn't seem right to sell it somehow, although in this small room it has never looked at home.'

Willy thumbed his nose. No talk of any offers—he doubted if anyone else had seen it. In fact, by a miracle, no one ever had—no one who could have recognized it for what it really was. Old girl may take a bit of persuading, he thought. The old man's the one to get at. He's all there for the money. I'll have a go at him.

'Well, Mr Kidley. I think I would like to buy it for my friend. What sort of price would you and your wife take for it?'

The old man was pleased to be brought back into things again. He had been left right out while his wife told her tale.

'Oh—arh—hum, let's zee now—doän know as 'ow we really knows what us *do* want vor'n. What do'ee zay, Ma? Think the gen'leman best make us an offer, doän you, Ma?'

Willy cut in. 'I'll take a chance on being able to pass it on to my friend —must be worth twenty-five pounds to him—or anybody else interested in Victorian furniture if it comes to that. I will give you one hundred and twenty-five pounds for this cabinet and the two chairs out in the hall.'

All this was said quickly, the two lots being cunningly coupled together—cabinet and chairs. He was supposed to have already bought the two chairs, but now gave the impression that the whole deal would rest on the hundred and twenty-five pounds being accepted for both lots.

Mrs Kidley looked at her husband, who was hopping about from one foot to another, having already spent the money in his mind.

"Tiz vor youm ter zay, Ma.' Wisely, he threw the decision back on to his wife. He'd had some of that in the past. When any decision he had made turned out wrong he had been the one to get it in the neck good and proper. Let her decide.

Willy introduced his 'flash'—the huge roll of fivers. 'I've got more money on me than I thought . . . five . . . ten . . . fifteen . . . twenty . . . twenty-five, thirty . . . yes, I must have over one hundred and fifty pounds here. I'll tell you what I'll do—make it a level one hundred and thirty. I'm very pleased with those two oak chairs.'

The sight of all those notes being slowly counted was too much for Mrs Kidley. Goodbye, cabinet—goodbye, Grandma. Hope you don't mind me selling it, but the money will bring Ted and me a few luxuries in our old age.

'Ah well, I suppose I had better say yes. I'll miss the old china-cabinet —not that I have ever had much in the way of china to put in it.'

'Miss having to dust it too, I expect,' said Willy with a laugh, still keeping the pressure on so that the old girl didn't change her mind and go back on the deal. He counted out the money on to the table then handed it to Mrs Kidley.

'Perhaps your husband would like to check it to see that the amount is correct?'

The old man looked a bit awkward. He was all right up to fifty, but got a bit wobbly after that figure.

'Take y' word vor it an' oi reckons.' One hundred pounds for his two chairs and the missus with thirty pounds for the cabinet!—he had never been so excited in all his life.

Meanwhile Willy had quickly written out a receipt, put on a stamp and proffered it to Mrs Kidley for her signature.

'. . . "*Received from Mr W. Shaun the sum of one hundred and thirty pounds, being the purchase price of two oak chairs and one giltwood china-cabinet. I hereby certify that these items are my property and that I have the right to dispose of them. I further state that I am very satisfied with the price which I have received for the above items*" . . . I don't think I have ever signed anything like this before—like a legal document.'

'I'm a business man, madam. This is a business man's way of doing things. If by chance I had an accident on the way home, and the items got damaged, this proves my legal right to make a compensation claim for the amount I paid.'

This was all blarney, but armed with a receipt of that nature he was safeguarded against all comers.

'Thank you, Mrs Kidley.' Willy hah-ed on the wet ink, folded the receipt, and put it in his wallet. Old Mr Kidley was still walking round the room with the bundle of notes in his hand, muttering inaudibly to himself: ''Underd pound vor them two chairs—'underd pound vor them two chairs!'

Willy glanced at the cabinet again. It's mine, mine, mine to do what I like with! The rarest piece I'll ever possess. A Chinese Chippendale pagoda cabinet! No doubt about it—absolutely right, especially in view of the history the old girl has given with it. Lord Abercoombey? Must look him up in *Burke's Peerage* as soon as I get home. What a cop for a hundred and thirty nicker!

'Oh, by the way, could you possibly get someone local here to give me a hand to load these things on to my car? I have it up the other end of the village—must not lift too much myself after my attack. It will save me having to make arrangements with carriers if I take them now. I never trust carriers—they always seem to break things.'

Old Ted nodded, consulting a large turnip watch in his waistcoat pocket. 'Ten t' twelve now. 'Nother ten minutes an' Bob'll be back from th' brick kilns for 'iz dinner. 'Ee'll give'ee a 'and on wi'un. Me, I'm too old.'

'I should think you are,' said Willy slyly. 'You must be seventy at least.'

'Zeventy? Me zeventy? Whoi, I be nigh on heighty-vor.'

The old man was tickled pink. 'Thurz Bob now. 'Eard 'im put 'iz bike in th' shed.'

Old Mr Kidley went through the kitchen out into the back garden. Willy could hear him calling Bob. The mutter of voices became louder and plainly audible as father and son came into the kitchen.

'Whaat? Hunderd quid for them two old oak chairs? The bloke must be nuts.'

'Ssh! 'Ee be thur in the vront room.'

Bob, a tubby, fiftyish man, more like his father than his mother, bounced into the room.

'Owld fah-de-dah goin' vor good then, Ma?' To Willy: 'Oi 'ear az 'ow you bin 'avin' a bit of a deal with the volks.'

Mrs Kidley looked a trifle sad.

'Dad do zay y' want a 'and out w' thiz cabinet. Woän take long. I've moved it afore.'

Willy suddenly remembered his heart condition.

'Wait a moment. I am unable to lift. You will have to get someone else as well.'

'Teddy 'Iggins just gorn indoors over th' roäd. Slip over and ask 'im t' lend a 'and, Bob.'

Father followed son outside. 'Got a bad 'eart' drifted in quite audibly. 'Dang noigh passed owt on us this marning. Thot us 'ood 'ave' t' 'ave the doctor to 'un. Cum an' zat down inzide wi' a glass of water. Perked up a bit arter a whoil. That's wen 'ee zeed thur chairs. Tuk izzelf a real vancy to 'em 'ee did an' not 'arf. 'Underd quid an' oi zayz t' . . .'

The conversation faded as they came indoors. Mrs Kidley started to empty the cabinet and Willy strolled up the road towards his car.

Coming back into the room once again, he cast his eyes over the contents of the cabinet, now jumbled together on the table underneath the window. Lot of junk, nothing there. Wonder what happened to the pieces of glass and china her grandmother chose?

The cabinet was more awkward than heavy, but Bob and the man from over the road managed at last to get it out. Twice Willy nearly had a real heart attack. Once when his precious cabinet was almost dropped and again when manoeuvring through the door it was tilted over at an alarming angle. One of the doors sprang open, and would have smashed itself off the hinges had Willy not anticipated this happening. He steadied it just in time, breaking out into a cold perspiration as he did so.

He had already prepared a good bed of wrappers in the roof rack, and up the cabinet went.

'Buyin' vurnitur yor bus'niss?' queried Bob with a keen look at the car.

'No, not really. Do it mostly for a hobby. What made you think that?'

'All them wrappers. Looks as if y' cum prepared.'

'Oh, them! As a matter of fact I've just delivered some corrugated-iron sheets to a friend of mine. I used the wrappers to stop the clatter. Must have overstrained the old ticker through lifting them. I felt rotten

F

on the way home and stopped the car, thinking that a slow walk and some fresh air might make me feel better. Your parents were very considerate.'

Bob helped tie the cabinet on—not too tightly, Willy made sure of that.

''Ope owld Neller, th' local cop, doãn zee you w' this thing on board. You'm brekkin th' lor wi' an over'ang this wide.'

Willy shrugged. He did not care two figs for the local law. He tested the ropes, intending to crawl home at a snail's pace so that there would be little risk of it coming off.

'Thanks very much—both of you.'

Two ten-shilling notes crackled as they were pushed into two trouser pockets.

Higgins went back indoors to tell his wife of the quickest and easiest ten bob he had ever earned in his life.

The two oak chairs were carefully stowed on the back seat with a lot of fuss going on to ensure they did not rub together. Very precious those two chairs were to Willy—destined for the Torminster sale-rooms, where he did not expect them to realize more than twenty-five shillings the two.

The Kidleys waved him off, and all the curtains of the cottages nearby were carefully and unobtrusively dropped back into place.

Willy arrived home just after 1 p.m., only realizing as he turned in through his gates that he was supposed to be feeling bad. All the way home his mind was far too occupied to think about his tummy which was better now, and telling him that a breakfast had been missed.

'Have you been drinking?'

Ethel had watched his arrival and the flush on his face, which only this morning had been as pale as a maggot, had not gone unnoticed.

'Me? Drinking? Certainly not. I've not touched a drop. What I *have* done is made myself the best day's work I'll ever do in my life—worth thousands and bought for nothing almost, a mere hundred and thirty. I could do with something to eat, dear. I'm starving.'

Ethel gave a hand to unload the prize. Into the front room it went and down came the Venetian blinds. No chances were going to be taken. No odd snooping dealer was going to set his eyes on that lot.

The whole afternoon was spent on research. A book containing extracts from *Chippendale's Directoire* showed a similar type of cabinet, but not so ornate or intricate—certainly no Chinese mirror pictures, which must have been specially made to order in China for

Willy's cabinet. The bells were definitely silver, and by an interesting maker. *Burke's Peerage* revealed that the Abercoombey title was now extinct.

Willy had made up his mind what he was going to do with the cabinet. There was only one man in England for it, one right at the top of the antique dealers' tree, whose name was only coupled with the finest and the best. If he did not want it there was always Hagar to fall back on.

Willy sent his letter off that evening in an envelope marked 'Very Private and Confidential'.

Dear Sir,

I am in possession of and wish to sell a very rare item of mid-eighteenth-century English furniture. Any information which I could now give might, by accident, pass into wrong hands, therefore no details are enclosed. Would you contact me, but not by telephone please. As you can see by the enclosed card, I am in the antique trade.

Yours faithfully,
William Shaun

'That ought to fetch them down, even if it's only out of curiosity.'
It did.

Late the next afternoon Ethel answered a knock on the front door. A quietly well-dressed man raised his hat.

'Good afternoon. Would it be Mrs Shaun?'

'Yes, that's right.'

'Could I see your husband, please—Mr William Shaun?'

Ethel took stock of her visitor—looked to her like an office pimp—some Government ministerial nuisance perhaps.

'He's out,' she replied, rather curtly.

'Could you give me any idea when he is likely to be at home?'

'I'm afraid I can't—probably not until this evening. He's away on business. Can I help you?'

A shadow of irritation flashed across the face of the visitor. (Damn the man! He *would* be out. Means hanging round this dump for hours. Can't go back into Torminster—have every dealer in the place wondering what the hell I'm here for!)

'Would you please tell your husband if he returns before I do that the gentleman in London he wrote to yesterday has come down to see him?'

Protocol forbade him asking to see this secret piece of furniture. Had he done so he would have met with a point-blank refusal. Ethel knew the drill.

'Crumps!' said Willy when he got home. 'He's come down mighty quick! Funny how the chance of buying a good lot, perhaps for nothing, gets them out of London. What time did he say he was coming back?'

He had just finished washing when the front-door bell rang. He answered it himself and asked him in. Again the same politeness, the impeccable manners.

'Let's get down to business straight away,' said Willy, opening the front-room door and following his visitor into the room. His sharp eyes noted the change of expression as two rapidly calculating and knowledgeable eyes flew straight to the pagoda cabinet.

'Is this what you wrote about?'

'Yes, that's it.' (Not giving much away by his expression now—face like a poker player.)

'I would like to make a detailed examination. Would you pull up the blinds? It is rather dark in here. Ah, that is better—now, if you would kindly pull the cabinet out from the wall—let me give you a hand—thank you. That is far enough out for me to examine the back.

'Hm . . . Yes.' His piercing blue eyes took in every detail. Wear and tear in the right places. Gilding worn down and away on vulnerably exposed spots; slight damage to the foliage; glazing bars on the doors correct. Hinges original and right for period; steel hand-made screws. Dirt and grime on the pagoda roofs towards the back where the duster seldom went. Toolmarks still visible on the undercutting, which had *not* been gilded. The right type of fixing for the glass, which was also original throughout, showing the whorls and irregularities of English glass of that period. The Chinese mirror-paintings did not need a second glance—no copyist or faker could have achieved that wonderful Oriental proportion and freedom of movement.

Slowly he walked round the cabinet, examining every square inch. Having finished with the back—down on his knees with head completely underneath, a powerful torch probing into every corner.

It was at this point Willy noticed the bright purple socks. Up to that moment he had felt self-conscious in the presence of the great one, but the man was human after all.

The examination took over half an hour, during which neither of them spoke. At last the silence was broken.

'I am satisfied with the condition. Before we proceed, will you give me some details regarding the cabinet?'

'There is certain information I am not prepared to give, but otherwise go ahead and ask me what you want to know about it.'

'How do you come to have this in your possession? I am not being inquisitive, neither have I any inclination to pry into your business, but I must know.'

'I thought you would ask me that, sir. The answer is—I bought it. What I gave for it and who I bought it from is my business. It came privately—not from another dealer, but, providing I have certain assurances from you, and, of course, providing you have purchased it, I am prepared to give you all the information I have been able to find regarding its past history. But one thing I will tell you now, and that is, it has a pedigree.'

This answer seemed to satisfy the London dealer—temporarily.

'How much do you want for it?'—the all-important question—a voice like silk, smooth, even, no hurry, no enthusiasm, giving nothing away.

Willy took a deep breath. Little beads of perspiration gathered on his temples. His shirt was damply clinging to his back. This was it. This the business. A mistake now could spoil the deal. Too much? Too little? Looking the man in the eye, he matched his tone with his.

'Six thousand.'

There was a silence; then the dealer slowly turned towards the cabinet. Meanwhile Willy waited.

The details and proportion were once again examined. Standing there was the finest Chippendale pagoda cabinet he would ever have the opportunity to buy—and he knew it. The firm had sold two in the past, but not like this one. There was no fault to be found with it, apart from minor damage which was to be expected. It was near enough mint condition and the only one he knew to have an original set of Chinese mirror-paintings. The value? How could one value it? It would depend on the depth of a collector's pocket. It was of very little consequence what he paid for it, within the limits of reason. He had paid more than the sum being asked for other rare objects. It was a question which of four customers should be allowed to possess it. Six thousand pounds? The man beside him did not deserve it. What did he know about dealing in fine antiques? What did he know of having thousands and thousands of pounds at risk in stock whose market value was tossed up and down like a cork in the troubled waters of slumps, trade recessions, currency de-valuations, customs restrictions and tense international situations? Local dealer—only guessing at its value—probably not even absolutely certain that it *was* really genuine. What could he get for it? Ten thousand? Yes, fairly sure of doing so.

'Five is my price. You can take it or leave it, Mr Shaun. It is a fair one. I am not proposing to haggle with you, but I have to sell it again.'

'Done,' said Willy, with a hand streaking out like a greyhound from the traps.

'Wait. Before we conclude the deal I want to know where that cabinet came from and how you came to buy it.'

He was taking no chances that the cabinet had been sold by some absconding butler in the absence of his employer.

'Well, sir, it is like this. If you start tracing up the history of this piece of furniture too closely you may release a nasty smell, figuratively speaking. I didn't overbid myself when I bought it. For me it was a gamble. If right, I stood to make a lot of money—wrong, then I would have lost more than I care to think about. If the people I bought it from hear what I sold it for there will be a bit of a rumpus.'

The other nodded. Just what I thought. Gambling on it. Gave about a hundred for it I should think. That's not my worry. I'm buying it for five thousand, and that's a fair enough price. I'll make sure he purchased it legally, though. . . . Too risky for us to advertise the cabinet under these circumstances. Pity, it would have looked wonderful splashed across the front page of the *Connoisseur*.

'You said it had a pedigree?'

Willy gave him all the details as told by Mrs Kidley, adding his own findings regarding the Abercoombey family. This seemed to satisfy his customer, who nodded when Willy produced the signed receipt, covering up the name with his thumb. He produced his cheque-book and sat down at the table. Sometimes weeks, months, elapsed before he paid for what he had bought, but this one was different. Bought and paid for it was his.

'Who do I make out the cheque to?'

'W. Shaun will do, thank you. . . . Thank you very much, sir. Do you want a receipt?'

'No. The cheque is enough. It needs a stamp on the back. I see you have one or two other nice little pieces here. That wine-cooler over there, for instance. From the look of things they're not, I take it, for sale?'

Willy shook his head. He had noted the interest in the wine-cooler. It was a good one of the Hepplewhite period with a finely proportioned domed lid. The unusual feature was the two-tiered stand on which it rested. He had 'held it away' from all other dealers in a certain knockout for one hundred and thirty-six pounds. Too much money, according to the others, who were pleased to broadcast the fact that Shaun had been dropped with a hot wine-cooler. Willy had not minded. His knockout pile was getting too big, and it was sound policy to invest it in fine antiques.

'Not at the moment, sir. If I ever get hard up or want some money quickly perhaps I'll let you know.'

It was no good asking what he would give for it. Dealers do their own reckoning and it is not customary for one to make an offer to another. Knowledge is sometimes hard bought and brain-picking has little chance of succeeding. The art of selling lies in the ability to judge what others are prepared to pay—and of buying, the guessing of the lowest price the seller will take.

'Can I offer you something to drink, sir?'

'No, thank you all the same, Mr Shaun. I must return to London now. Our van will come down for the cabinet tomorrow. In the meanwhile please do not show it or let it be seen by anyone else, nor give any information regarding this purchase. We on our side will make no disclosures other than those relating to the Abercoombey family. Secrecy is desirable for obvious reasons.'

The two shook hands. The deal had been concluded. Five-thousand-poorer departed for London in the Rolls-Royce which had been parked well up the road towards the village. He was more than satisfied, he was delighted. What he had just bought was practically unique. The firm was used to paying huge prices for the finest pieces in the London auction rooms. This was always a good advertisement, but the trouble with that sort of buying was that all one's customers knew exactly what one had given, consequently only a small working turnover profit could be expected, or else the thing had to be hidden away, sometimes for years, until the details of the purchase were forgotten. Buying on commission was even less profitable. However, now and again a plum dropped off the tree and a fine antique could be acquired without anyone of consequence knowing what it had cost. This gave a chance of being able to make a big profit out of it. The pagoda cabinet was a good, ripe, juicy plum, acquired without having to shake the tree, either.

Five-thousand-richer grabbed his wife and danced her round the kitchen table.

'I've sold it! I've sold it! Five thousand smackers! Five thousand!'

'*How* much?' almost shrieked Ethel.

Her husband had mentioned a hope of getting thousands for it but she had dismissed this as just another dealer's pipe-dream.

'Five thousand, dear! We are on the way to the big shop yet.'

Willy sobered down when he thought of the lurker in the background—always present, always there. 'Income tax. They'll knock a hole out of it. Why do people have to make out cheques "Account payee only"? Come to think of it, I'd've had to put it through the bank, anyway—nobody round here would cash one that big. Put my year's trading profit at well over eight thousand. Have to pay a packet of tax on that lot and nothing much I can do about it either.'

'Won't they let you spread it over a few years so that if you have a bad year the good ones will offset it?'

'Not on your nelly! They're out for every blinking penny they can get. I think we'll get ourselves another car—a good one, too. I've had the Austin now for just over six years. It was 1947 I bought it. She's still good but shabby. That will help. Get twenty-five per cent depreciation allowance on that. I'm also going up to London to buy every decent reference book I can lay my hands upon, providing I can get a back-dated receipt—"purchase of reference books" put down on the accounts for a date prior to this deal will have to be allowed. There is a set of books on furniture and another one on clocks by the same author which I've always wanted. Not much change out of a hundred for them. In fact there are dozens of books I want and I'm jolly well going to do myself some good by having them. I'd rather see them on my bookshelves than see the money go straight down the drain on ground-nut schemes or some other such tomfoolery.'

'Yes, dear,' was Ethel's safe answer.

7   The New Cadillac

Not long afterwards, Willy was taking a stroll round his domain, before going to the local sale-room. Across the fields, pale stubble and fresh green kale, the woods were a warm russet brown and gold, and the distant humped patchwork of the foothills rose steeply to the blue line of the moors. He felt in a mellow autumnal mood for once, conscious of his own golden harvest—the five thousand pounds safely banked in Tor-minster. Not a bad little property, he thought with satisfaction, looking back at the house, the herbaceous border (most of it cared for on expenses, too!) and the few late roses. Be a nice little nest-egg for Ann one day, always supposing they settled here (and it was at that moment that the seeds of an idea, a future plan for expansion, first took root in his fertile mind). She had nearly finished her time at the expensive private school he'd managed to send her to as a day-boarder. What now? She was developing into a lovely young woman—always surrounded by a pack of gangling gawky adolescents, atrociously dressed and with manners to match. Let alone older men. . . . He'd have to keep an eye on her.

He went to the garage and backed out his new Cadillac estate wagon, all purple and chromium and low slinky lines, until lately the pride and joy of Lieut.-Colonel Hiram J. Stout, U.S.A.F. His friend Bruno Hammers, a garage owner, had sold it to him in part exchange for his old Austin, a complicated sale which was carefully designed to benefit themselves and deprive their arch-enemy, the Commissioners of Inland Revenue.

Purring on his way to Torminster, Willy's feeling of general well-being was increased by the memory of a conversation they'd had over a number of double whiskies. Bruno's trouble, it seemed, was that he had too much cash. He'd done very well for himself in the war-years; part of his garage had been taken over by a Ministry and, in a key administrative position himself, he had been exempt from war-service and able to keep up his own business. He had a petrol storage tank that hardly anyone knew about—*and* he somehow kept it filled. The few officials who did know profited by the knowledge and kept their mouths shut. Every transaction was cash, no cheques, no accounts.

'And there it is,' went on Bruno. 'Trouble is, I just don't know what to do with it. Got it hidden away here there and everywhere—enterprising burglar could swipe the lot. Friend of mine's put a lot of his money into this antique stuff. Frankly I don't understand a thing about it—not interested.'

'Good safe way of salting away your cash, B.H. Say you buy a new car—telly—carpets—too much of an obvious splash—you'll soon have awkward questions asked. But buy antiques and "they" are up the monkey tree. You or your wife could always have been left them by an aunt. My advice is, don't buy locally, always pay cash, and unless it's someone you know, use a dud name. If you're going in for it, put your money into good stuff, up in the hundreds or more, don't mess about with small-time antiques. The better the quality the better the value will hold.'

'All right, Shaun, you know a thing or two. You find me a few pieces—something that'll look good and be an investment.'

'Sure, B.H. I'll remember you the next good lot I get. Silver's a good proposition, too. Doesn't take up much room, easily hidden, easily transported, easily got rid of. Mind you, what I bring over will be pricey —top-notch stuff always is.'

Willy made a mental note to drop on B.H. the next hot lot he got landed with in the knockout. How wonderful to have a wealthy punter behind him who didn't know Chippendale from his Aunt Fanny! They parted on good terms, Willy with his new purple and chromium Cadillac estate car and B.H. with well over four hundred profit.

Worming his way through the crowd of people in the local sale-room, he at last found Reg.

'Hullo, Reg! Any of the London crowd turned up yet? Too much to hope that they would miss a decent pair of Sheraton card-tables.'

'Haven't seen any of them, Willy, no prices left on the books either, as far as I can find out. The porters are clear too. We may have them all to ourselves yet. Is Tom here?'

'Yes, he's around somewhere. I saw him a moment or so ago. How many of us are there here?'

'Counting the hangers-on, I should think about fifteen or sixteen. Some of them won't reckon the tables much above a hundred. Should be some decent K.O. money today, keep our fingers crossed.'

Willy wriggled back up the sale-room, passing in front of Jo.

'Hallo, Jo. I've been meaning . . .'

'How did you get on with it, Willy?'

'Nothing like hinting for your commission. I've got something for you—let you have it later outside.'

Voice from the door—'How far's he got?'

'He is only selling Lot 130.'

'Hell, only Lot 130? Half an hour over the last eighteen lots? What's he up to?'

'Hanging out for shilling bids on every lot. Seen any of the London boys?'

'Not a sign of one so far. Another twenty-one lots to go yet. Be about another hour, I suppose.'

Willy sauntered down the steps into the yard, eventually followed by Jo. He had been thinking about the question of Jo's commission on the Chinese Chippendale cabinet ever since the deal was concluded. Now he had to make up his mind.

How much do I give him? By rights he is entitled to two hundred and fifty pounds and I would not begrudge him that either. The trouble is he can't keep his great mouth shut. The whole world would soon know he had put me in the way of a terrific deal and that he had two hundred and fifty as his commission. Everyone would know where I bought the gilt cabinet—a cabinet so wonderful that even the runner had two hundred and fifty out of it. No. Jo will have to pay the price of being unable to keep private business to himself. 'Oh, there you are, Jo.'

'Did you buy it?'

'Mm. I bought it. I don't know why you got yourself so worked up about it, though. Only Victorian—about 1850. Good export lot. Had to give thirty quid for it. Couldn't buy it from the old faggot for less than that. I've sold it and got a normal profit. Here's fifty bob for yourself, Jo—smart of you spotting it like that.'

Jo pocketed the money, slightly disappointed. He had no idea what period the cabinet was, but somehow it had looked like a good lot.

'Thanks, Willy. Every little helps as the old woman said as she did her——'

'Hey, Willy! Better come on up. He's only three lots away now,' Tom shouted from the bottom of the stairs.

'Hallo, Tom. How's the game?'

'Same as usual. Can't find anything with any meat left on the bone.'

'Please, gentlemen. Quiet at the back there! Any advance on thirty shillings and I'm selling at thirty shillings to the bidder at the back—it's against you now, madam. One more bid, shall I say? Have you all done at thirty shillings and I'm selling at thirty shillings, thirty-two-and-six, any advance on thirty-two-and-six and I'm selling at thirty-two-and-six. Have you all done? I'm selling. I'm selling'—Bang!—'Sold!'

'What name, madam? Sturbey? How do you spell it? S.T.U.R.B.E.Y. Thank you.'

He heaved a sigh; money was being hard-earned this morning.

'Now let's see. Next lot. Ladies and gentlemen, Lot 152. "Pair of mahogany and inlaid Sheraton period card tables, with fold-over tops, baize-lined, and standing on square taper legs terminating in spade feet." Now, ladies and gentlemen. These are a very fine pair, very fine indeed. Who will start me at one hundred?'

'Fifteen pounds'—Ropey's voice from back left-hand side.

'Forty pounds'—the auctioneer's own bid. He did not know the real value of the pair but had no intention of selling them under fifty pounds. There was no need to dwell with the bidding on this lot. The trade were there at the back of the sale-room. The bidding would be fast.

By two-pound advances it was Ropey's bid at fifty pounds. In vain the auctioneer cast round for an advance. The seven or eight knowledge-able antique traders at the back were just congratulating themselves on having eighty pounds or so to divide later on in the settlement when 'Fifty-two pounds!' came from a loud clear voice right at the back by the door.

With one accord sixteen men spun round.

'Oh, blimey!' muttered Reg. 'That stinker here again?'

'That stinker' was a private buyer who had recently moved into the district—a man called Starling who was detested by the local dealers because he had set himself to overbid them on nearly every decent piece of antique furniture which had turned up in the sale-rooms during the last three months. Two or three times he had been forced out of the bidding when opposed by strong London traders, relinquishing only at a price which left nothing for the local boys in the knockout afterwards. Salt had been rubbed into their wounds with the rumour that this knowall was one of the clever dicks who write articles and books on how clever they have been to acquire this and that and beat all the dealers at the same time.

Slowly the bidding went up to one hundred pounds by two-pound advances—Ropey bidding the round figure. There was no pause from the doorway, however, and the auctioneer took advantage of the strong competition to increase the advances to five pounds.

'One hundred and five bid. One hundred and five. Any advance on one hundred and five?'

Ropey adopted delaying tactics, holding out on his bid until the last moment, just as the hammer was about to descend. He was getting near the limit. On his reckoning the pair of tables were worth one hundred and twenty-five pounds. It was his bid at one hundred and twenty but still the bidding was advanced from the doorway.

By this time everyone in the saleroom was turning their heads backwards and forwards from one bidder to the other and then to the auctioneer. At this last bid Ropey shook his head. He was through. Willy took it up with a slight flick of his catalogue.

'One hundred and thirty bid. One hundred and thirty bid. One hundred and thirty-five'—again the flick—'one hundred and forty.'

Tom, standing behind Willy, quietly said: 'O.K., Willy. I'm in with you to one hundred and sixty.'

'Thanks, Tom, just what I reckoned them myself.'

'Count me in too,' said Reg, who was standing by the side of Tom. 'If the three of us are in let's take it up to one hundred and ninety. There won't be any profit but we cannot lose much. London trade are bound to buy them at a hundred and seventy-five. I've seen better but they are a clean pair.'

These three would willingly and deliberately have cut one another's throats in the knockout on the pair of tables, had there been a knockout. As there was not going to be one they presented a united front against the common foe.

At every bid Willy made, Peter Nebbing, who was almost dancing with rage as he saw his chances of drawing a couple of pounds completely disappear, was saying: 'Go to it, Shaun! Good old Shaun! Slam into him—make him pay! Go on, man—give him another!' He had no stake in the outcome—what was it to him if Shaun overbid himself and got a hot lot round his neck?

Willy bid the limit, going one more for luck, but couldn't hold the pair of tables. At two hundred pounds they were knocked down to the gentleman standing in the doorway, who was named as the buyer.

There was a general rustle of appreciation amongst the audience, half of whom were the regular 'sit-and-see' type. For them it had been a good fight and something to go home and talk about. By the time the auctioneer was halfway through selling the next lot all the dealers were noisily making their way out of the sale-room—too fed up to bother about going out quietly. There were one or two nondescript pieces of antique bric-à-brac coming up later, but not worth stopping for. All the morning wasted and no knockout money—no tables.

Reg, Tom, and the two Trewens were more furious than Willy, having been beaten on their own home ground—a bad advertisement, but there was a limit.

'Just have to put a stop to that blighter Starling, somehow. Haven't been able to get hold of a decent lot in the sale-rooms since he has been around. Doesn't give us a chance.'

'What the devil can we do about it? There's no stopping him.'

'He paid through the nose for them, anyway.'

'That's beside the point. The point is we didn't get anything out of them, not even the satisfaction of having them for sale. They were a good pair and would have cost him more than two hundred in London—he knows it, too.'

'You are right there, Reg, but I have a cracking idea,' said Willy. 'What about Bert Hammond's table?'

(Bert Hammond's table was almost a legend in the South and West of England since it had turned up at a small private sale just over a year ago, catalogued as a 'superb Chippendale period mahogany pie-crust-edged table, on fluted and carved pillar supported by tripod legs terminating in ball-and-claw feet. The legs and pillar carved with acanthus-leaf foliage and intricate scrollwork.' This lot by itself was sufficient to bring the trade flocking to the sale. The table looked even better than described. The colour and patination were superb and the general condition faultless —not even the odd wormhole in the pine block forming the top layer of the 'birdcage' or 'castle' which supported the pie-crust top on the pillar. As there had been very little opposition the table went for the sum of eighty-two pounds.

Willy had it marked in his catalogue three hundred and seventy-five pounds. Tom had three hundred and fifty pounds. A rough forecast gave ten pounds each for those left in the second round and a certainty of not holding it against the London crowd. The table was 'London goods'. In the second round of the knockout, however, one of the top London dealers 'faded' at one hundred and sixty-two pounds, leaving the bidding with Bert Hammond. Willy and Tom, realizing immediately that something must be radically wrong with the table, something which had escaped their notice and knowledge, also 'faded', together with the other London dealers and everyone else. There were quite a few puzzled expressions but one by one, as it came to their turn to advance the bidding, declined and 'went out' leaving the table with Bert Hammond, who had to pay out eighty pounds and then pay the bill for the table.

Bert was more perplexed than anyone. He had reckoned the table at well over three hundred—had thought it quite safe to go to that figure with no risk of holding it.

After all the settling up, for his own education Willy quietly contacted the London dealer who had been standing next to Bert and who had thrown nearly every other dealer into confusion by his ducking the bidding.

'Hallo, Mr Haltain, do you mind doing me a favour? Tell me what is wrong with that pie-crust.'

'Ah-hah! So it sucked you in too? That table seems to have sucked in a good many. They faded just like a lot of sheep when I ducked out—not knowing why and not trusting to their own knowledge. The table is one of the cleverest fakes I've ever come across and I have seen a good many in my time. One or two of us here knew it, of course, but after all we had to earn a bob or two and it was obvious that the rest of you were all set for a good go on it. It was no gamble to land it on to someone not quite so learned as ourselves. It was a certainty. What did you reckon it, Shaun?'

'Three hundred and fifty.'

'Ha, had it been right you would not have been near it. Seven-fifty, more like it. Wish I had gone on a bit longer in the knockout with it now.'

'In what way is it a fake? Hang it all, I examined that table inside out and I couldn't see anything wrong with it.'

'That's the clever part. The table itself *is* old—large common-or-garden mahogany round-topped gipsy table with thick vase-shaped turned pillar and thick tapered legs which terminated in broad pad feet—you know the sort.'

Willy nodded. He often bought them. They were mid-eighteenth century—good export line. The trade always wanted them. Ten to twelve pounds apiece usually.

'The top was reduced in diameter, shaped to the pie-crust pattern and the mahogany scooped out, leaving the top thinner and with a raised pie-crust edging. The clever fiend who did it used old hand-tools as well. So much for the top, the underside of which showed every indication of its proper age. The block and birdcage were left intact—absolutely genuine Chippendale period. The thickness of the pillar was reduced, the lumpy vase shape allowing plenty of scope for good deep crisp carving of the foliage. The legs were thinned down, also leaving room for the same type of carving. Now we come to the cleverest piece of faking that I have ever seen. These tables which have been "carved up" afterwards give themselves away on the ball-and-claw feet. To carve it out of the ordinary pad foot always leaves the ball and claw slender, with the appearance of the claws slipping off the ball, and the ball itself half, and sometimes not even half, a ball.

'The man who did this job got over that difficulty by a very clever piece of cabinet-making—splicing a piece of mahogany of the same grain and colour on to each side of all three pad feet by means of a double butt-jointed splice, and that *is* cabinet-making, that is! This gave him plenty of depth on which to carve a good substantial ball and claw, the claws gripping the ball as though they meant to do so. The join was completely hidden between each outside claw. Very clever! *Very* clever! The whole table, apart from the under-surface, was given a coat of Spanish lacquer. It was then rubbed and polished down on all vulnerable surfaces, leaving them glowing in golden highlight whilst all recesses remained the darker colour—giving the whole a wonderful patina. As some of the original period furniture was treated in this way one couldn't condemn it on that point.

'What gave it away, however, was the proportion. The height of the legs, compared with the height of the pillar, was not good enough proportion for a fine craftsman. The birdcage, being the original left from the larger table, was much too big for the pie-crust top—out of proportion again. It was a good maxim: if you see one fault start looking for others. Once the table was turned upside down and the bottom of the feet exposed, the splicing could be seen. But I still take my hat off to the man who did it—must have taken him weeks. The joints could only just be seen and then only if you were looking for them. They could not be seen anywhere from the top of the ball and claw.'

With due thanks murmured for pounds-worth of education and knowledge, Willy returned to the sale-room. He wanted another look at that table. Sure enough, it was all there, just as had been explained.

'Well, what d'you know about that? Poor old Bert has copped a banger this time.'

Bert Hammond certainly had, much to the open amusement and glee of his fellow traders, who lost no time in telling him exactly what he had in the way of a fake piece of Chippendale furniture.

By the end of the week there was not a dealer in the South who didn't know all about Bert Hammond's table, so he couldn't pass it on.

For a whole year he had tried in vain to palm the table off on to some unsuspecting colleague. Those whose ignorance made them an open target were not the sort to be spending hundreds of pounds on any one piece of furniture. Those who did either recognized it for what it was or had already heard about the table. Bert had the sense to realize that a small country dealer could never get away with selling it to a private customer on the strength of a false representation of genuine antiquity. He still had the table. . . .)

'I don't follow you,' said Ropey. 'What about Bert Hammond's table?'

'Why not borrow it from Bert, stick it here in the sale-rooms in the hope of landing it on Mr Blinking Nuisance at a nice fancy price? If the job falls down we'll have to stump up a bit of commission to the auctioneer and Bert will have his table back again.'

'Well done, Willy, that's a good one!'

'Think it will work?'

G

'I don't see why not—highly improbable that he has ever called on Bert. The chances are he has not seen it.'

'The thing is, if we get it into the next sale, will he bid for it?'

'Hold it, you two. Not so fast! Think you can get that table into the sale without old Hickory smelling a rat? Not on your life! You know how fussy he is about selling traders' goods—always thinks there is something wrong with them.'

'He's right there—nearly always is!'

Tom thumbed his nose. 'I can get over that one. Got a customer— old Mrs Prater, who'd sell her soul for five bob. She works all the jumble sales and white elephant stalls—always bringing me in rubbish but now and again a good lot comes out of it. If Bert agrees, I suggest we put it in her house. She can then come to the auctioneer with a yarn about all the dealers pestering her to sell her mahogany table. That ought to arouse his interest. He loves to get one over on the antique dealers, and to take a lot like that away from them underneath their very noses—well, it's in the bag.'

'What did the table cost old Bert?'

'Stood him in at about one hundred and sixty pounds.'

'Think he would take a hundred?'

'He will have to take less than that. I will see if I can persuade him to let us have it on the understanding that if we sell it he gets seventy-five free. If we can't land it, he has it back, with no expense involved.'

'All right, Willy, you do that. You know him better than we do.'

'Now let's think it out properly. Take it for granted that we've got the table in the sale. It will be splashed in letters a yard wide in the catalogue. He's bound to have a go at it, but we've got to get organized.'

'Better cover the London boys. If they get wind of a lot like that they'll all be down here—might let the cat out of the bag.'

'How about having Jo Busting on the door for the whole of the view day? We can make it worth his while. He can tip the boys off about the table as they come in. We don't want them swearing about it in the sale-room.'

'I'd rather Croupy Gespott did it. Jo opens his mouth too wide.'

'O.K. Croupy it is. He will do it if he gets a quid out of it.'

'On view day Croupy can give you, Reg, the tip when Old Nuisance comes in. You ring Tom. I'll be around somewhere, and I'm sure Ropey will be in the town. Tom can ring you, Dickie, and you tell your brother.

We can then all "officially" view the sale—singly or in pairs. We all make a fuss of the table and make a good show of marking our catalogues. He will be watching us same as he was when we were looking at that pair of silver wine-coasters—he wouldn't have even seen them, let alone bought against us, had you not made such a fuss about looking up the hall-mark in your pocket book, Dickie—you silly ass!'

'That's all very well to say that, Willy. If you chaps had any decency in you you would have given me the tip-off. No, not you, not one of you; each and all of you hoping that the rest wouldn't notice them—just take them for Sheffield plate as described in the catalogue.'

'Time you knew your date-letters off by heart, Dickie. Fancy having to look them up in a book each time you see a piece of silver.'

'*You* can't afford to speak, Ropey. There's just as much water in between your ears as there——'

'O.K., you two—put a sock in it!—let's get back to business.'

'If he sees us crowding the table, he'll be on to it.'

'That's about all we can do, I guess.'

'It's worth trying, anyway.'

'What is it going to cost us if it doesn't come off?'

'Let's see. If we reckon on getting the table from Bert for seventy-five pounds and run it up near enough to one hundred and seventy-five, we will have to pay out about twenty-eight pounds in commission whether we drop it on him or not. There are seven of us here—four pounds apiece—that will not break anyone. On the other hand, if we manage to bring it off we will have about seventy-two pounds to divide between us after allowing for commission. Tenner each with—what did you say her name was, Tom . . . ?'

'Prater.'

'. . . oh yes, Mrs Prater having the couple of pounds for her part in the proceedings. The odds are two and a half to one in favour. Anybody want to back out?'

Three days later Willy strolled into Bert's shop. He was serving a customer so Willy kept in the background. Bert was trying very hard to sell a mid-nineteenth-century part tea service to a lady, sullying the name of Rockingham by applying it to a bit of Staffordshire at its lowest and worst. The customer was wavering. Willy made mental bets. She's going to buy it. No, she isn't. Yes, she is.

'Cheap for the price, madam. Where can you get a modern tea

service of this quality for fourteen pounds? I'm not making much profit on it—cost me twelve pounds.'

Willy gave Bert a silent reprimand: You made a blunder there, chum. Bet she won't buy it now. He was right. She didn't, leaving the shop saying she would think it over.

'Hullo, Willy. I wonder how I stick it at times. Had her here for nearly half an hour and then she couldn't make up her mind.'

'How are you, Bert? You have my sympathies, but if you don't mind me minding your business I will tell you something. She was right on the point of buying that service until you told her what you gave for it.'

'That's right, and it was the truth. I did give twelve pounds for it.'

'I don't disbelieve you, Bert—but *she* did! That's the important point. She could not believe that you would be content to make only two pounds on twelve. I was watching her face. If you were lying about the price, she thought, probably everything else you said about the service was untrue. See what I mean? I will never forget what old Abe Sitwell said to me when I was with my father in the Torminster shop— poor old Abe, he's dead now, but he got to the top of the tree before he died. "Never, *never* tell your customer, private or dealer, what you gave for anything you're trying to sell! It is none of their business what you have given—keep them guessing. The transaction rests on whether they are prepared to give what you are asking, or if they can beat you down to the price they want to pay—it rests on nothing else." Still, I didn't come to jaw like this, and it is nothing to do with me any- way. What I did come down for was to find out if you still had something. I see you still have—I mean your old friend the pie-crust table.'

'That blankety-blank thing? Yes. I've still got it. Why? Think you can find a home for it?'

'All depends, Bert. I have a good chance to sell it, but at a price. What sort of money are you prepared to lose on it?'

'Damn' thing cost me over a hundred and sixty quid. Bought it with my eyes shut, although at the time I was convinced it was a right one. Shook me rigid when it dropped on me. Thought it was safe for well over three hundred. I'm fed up with the thing, and a good loser. You can have anything you get over a hundred.'

'Sorry, Bert, you are still flying too high for me. I want the table for a special job and seventy-five would be tops. No good you trying to raise me—that's the limit and I'm still not absolutely certain that I can park it for you, but there is every chance. What about it?'

'I'll do the deal for seventy-five and glad to see the back of it. Please don't return it. Good luck.'

'Thanks, I will do my best. How much do you want for the three-colour Wedgwood jardinière? Haven't got the other one, I suppose? A singleton is not all that much use but it is three-colour Wedgwood— just blue and white or green and white and I would not be asking the price of it.'

Bert shook his head.

'No, only the one, but that is better than nothing. Twenty-two pounds ten.'

'Take twenty?'

This time Bert nodded. He had bought the Wedgwood jardinière privately, bought a pair of them, but one was cracked. He knew how useless it would be to display them as a pair with one cracked. Every dealer who saw them would shed trade tears over the damage and end up by not buying the perfect one. Displayed on its own the jardinière was flawless. He had succeeded in bleaching out the crack in the other one until it was hardly discernible. Three-colour Wedgwood was rare, and having sold his perfect specimen no doubt someone would buy the other for a pound or so.

Willy was pleased with his purchase. Bert had sold it cheap—too cheap. Certain tenner left in that one, he thought. Old Bert can't be very well up in this line.

'It *is* perfect, isn't it?' In his haste to buy Willy had for once forgotten to make a minute examination. All he had done was to turn the jardinière upside down to look for the mark WEDGWOOD in large capitals.

'As far as I know it is. Take a look and satisfy yourself. It was perfect when I bought it and no one else has seen it yet.'

Willy examined the jardinière.

'Yes, that's all right Bert. D'you mind giving me some paper to wrap it in?'

Bert did so, watching while Willy wrapped it up.

'Here, you'd better have a cardboard box to put it in—don't want it rolling about in the car. I've got one in the back room which will do the job nicely. Here, let's have it.'

Willy loaded the table and his cardboard box, well pleased with the afternoon's work.

Bert could scarcely believe his eyes when he saw the Cadillac.

'This *yours*? I don't believe it!' Shaun must be making money, real money, he thought, to be able to buy and run a car like this. Why, it was only a year or so ago he bought himself a small country mansion. Still, he works hard and he's as wily as a fox. He's not the only wily one, either.

Willy showed his piece of three-colour Wedgwood to Ethel when he got home. She admired the beautiful pastel-coloured decoration, but did not properly understand the rarity.

'You know it's cracked, I suppose?'

'Cracked? Cracked? It can't be. It was perfect when I bought it and it has been in a box on the seat all the way home. Let's see. You're right, dear. It *is* cracked! Now how the deuce could that have happened? Oh, *damnation*!'

Out in the back room of his shop Bert Hammond gave a sarcastic chuckle as he surveyed a perfect three-colour Wedgwood jardinière. That'll teach Shaun to go swanking round the countryside in new cars! He'll wonder how the devil it got cracked. It was perfect when he bought it. He made sure of that. Hope he sells it as perfect and then gets the crack pointed out by an angry customer. I'll have to keep this one out of sight—sell it direct to a Yankee china dealer and get it out of the country. Should get thirty pounds for it.

8 A Few Tricks Worth Knowing

Tom and Reg Bardon were busy talking in the alleyway of the yard which gave access to the sale-room. They had come to see Bert Hammond's pie-crust table—and also, they hoped, their enemy Starling—well and truly sold. Down the steps from the sale-room came Dickie Trewen.

'How far's he got, Dickie?'

'Oh, only Lot 84.'

'What? He was on Lot 60 nearly an hour ago. What's he up to?'

'Oh, I dunno—bit of a dispute over some lot or other—took them about a quarter of an hour to sort it out. Ended up by putting the lot under the hammer again. Jammed in there like sardines, they are. I hate sales on a wet day—place absolutely reeks of wet clothes and gumboots. Just look at this rain! You would think it would put people off and keep them at home, but there are as many in there as I've ever seen.'

'Whereabouts is he? We saw him go in.'

Everyone knew he meant the hated Starling.

'The last I saw of him was over by the far wall, standing up behind that three-piece suite. Here's Shaun and Ropey. No hurry yet, you chaps. He's only on Lot 84. I say, look! Here's Bert Hammond.'

They all stared at Bert as if he had come from the South Pole.

'I've got my sixpenny ticket for the Rogues' Gallery,' was Bert's cheery greeting. 'Hiya, boys! Surprised to see me? Thought you could keep that pie-crust table all to yourselves, eh? Reads like a good lot in the catalogue. I went a purler on one a year ago but I don't make the same mistake twice. Is there too much of a crush inside for me to get in and have a look at it?'

It was Ropey who broke the tongue-tied silence.

'Who said you haven't made the same mistake twice?'

'Whad'ya mean, "Haven't made the same mistake twice"?'

'*You* have,' said Ropey, a sarcastic grin drooping from the corner of his mouth.

'I give up. I don't know what you're getting at.' Bert was beginning to get huffy. He sensed Ropey was successfully taking the mickey out of him.

'You said you made a mistake on a pie-crust table and weren't going to make the same mistake twice. Well, you have. You've made a mistake coming up here to see it. Happens to be the only lot of any consequence in the sale and it also happens to be yours.'

'Mine? How do you mean, "mine"?'

'Yes, yours—your table. The one you let Willy have.'

'What the devil's going on? What's it doing here in this sale? Shaun, you were supposed to be selling it to some private customer.'

'I didn't say anything about a private customer, Bert. What I said to you, if you remember correctly, was that I thought I could sell it. That is exactly why it is in the sale today. We are going to sell it—we hope.'

'You don't mean to say I've fagged up here forty-odd mile just to take a gander at my own b——y table? Well, I go to —— sea. What's the game, that's what I want to know?'

Bert was gradually smoothed down as they explained. He was sport enough to enter into the spirit of the game.

'Well, blow me down! I hope it comes off.'

'Who's going to do the bidding?'

'Oh, let Willy do it, then we locals can keep right out of it.'

'What's the idea? He's only selling Lot 124. There's another eight lots to go yet. Hey, Peter, you silly mutt, what was the idea in bringing us up here in such a hurry? Nowhere near it yet.'

'I've lost sight of him.'

'Lost sight of who?'

'Why, Starling, of course. He was standing over there by that three-piece suite and suddenly he wasn't there. I can't see him anywhere else, either.'

Several pairs of keen eyes swept the sale-room, taking in all sitting and standing. Peter was quite right. The 'enemy' was nowhere to be seen, and he certainly had not left the sale-room.

'I know where he is,' said Reg. 'Been in the same place myself many times—so have you all. He's round behind the door just on the left of the rostrum—that little cubby-hole where the clerk sits and takes the money when the sale is over.'

'Of course! How stupid of us! What's he gone in there for?'

'That looks good to me,' said Willy. 'He has gone in there to do his bidding. Only the auctioneer and people sitting in the two front rows can see him. I think he realizes we are out gunning for him—most likely found out that the pair of card tables are not so cheap after all. I reckon he wants that pie-crust table and doesn't want us to know who is bidding. We'll soon find out.'

'*Quiet at the back, please, gentlemen!* If you want to carry on a conversation please do so outside or in between the selling of the lots, not whilst the actual bidding is in progress!' The auctioneer rapped out his reprimand.

'Lot 132, ladies and gentlemen. You have, no doubt, all seen this lovely little specimen of the Chippendale period. The best item we have today in this sale. "Lot 132. Chippendale mahogany pie-crust table." Who will start me at a hundred?'

'Twenty-five pounds,' from Willy at the back. It would have been silly, and against usual custom, to bid more than a quarter of the requested starting price; other people might get worked up into the bidding. The more the merrier in this case. The bidding got off with a rush, advances coming from all round the room. A number of people had taken a fancy to the table, but the bidding started to thin out by the time 'forty-six pounds' had been reached. It was Willy's bid at forty-eight. There was a pause. The auctioneer swept the crowd with a pair of eyes not likely to miss the slightest movement of eye, hand, or catalogue.

Was the enemy going to bid?

'Fifty pounds bid. Fifty pounds bid—fifty-two, fifty-two—fifty-four.' The battle was on, and the bidding became monotonous.

The whereabouts of the secret bidder was now obvious. People sitting in the first few rows were twisting their heads round as though they were following the ball at a tennis match.

There is far more to bidding than many people suppose. A good bridge-player nearly always makes a good bidder. When at a sale it is very easy to make a fool of yourself by bidding in a loud voice or wildly waving the catalogue. In the first place everyone will notice that you are bidding. Secondly, you will look very stupid if your bidding finishes in the shillings range and the lot ultimately ends up at hundreds of pounds. And people who until that moment had no interest in that particular lot may well bid it up against you for a variety of reasons—out of devilment, or the determination not to let that 'awful Mrs Brown' have the item cheaply, or because if you're so keen on it 'it must be good'—endless reasons in fact.

Sales in general would be far less monotonous if more variety was given to the bidding.

All the 'boys' in the trade could remember Jolly Boy Target, a dealer with the reputation of being a 'goer' when it came to buying in the sale-rooms. Unknown to the rest of his brethren Jolly Boy had a quiet arrangement with all the auctioneers in his locality. As long as his pipe was in his mouth he was bidding for the lot, and would continue to do so until he removed it. Many times he stood amongst his colleagues at the back of the sale-room quite openly bidding for some important lot. Having bid up to about half of what he was prepared to give he would shake his head, say in a loud voice: 'That's enough for me. Too hot now as far as I'm concerned,' stick his pipe in his mouth and take no more interest. The fact that Jolly Boy was 'out' was sufficient to shake the confidence of others who may have reckoned it at a higher figure. If Jolly Boy had 'finished' there wasn't much profit left in it. Perhaps a few half-hearted bids would follow, or maybe quite a number more, if there was stiff private opposition, but the lot invariably 'went out' to a 'private' buyer. It was a good dodge and lasted a few years. The fact that one day Jolly Boy inadvertently lit up his pipe at the back of the room and got himself landed with a very stained and dilapidated feather mattress was of little consequence.

But in the end suspicions were aroused, and J.B.'s little dodge discovered.

At 'One hundred pounds bid' it was against Willy, who now began to strengthen his opening gambit. The auctioneer was calling for a bid but he held back almost until the hammer was dropped. This was a trick he often used to put off inexperienced bidders, who were likely to interpret the pause as meaning that the price had almost reached Willy's limit. The ensuing bids would seem to be dragged out of the dealer, giving the idea that the lot had reached its full price and that whatever else was advanced would be above market value, the dealer just pushing up the price to have the satisfaction of making his opponent pay heavily for the triumph.

Willy guessed that 'Mr Nuisance Starling' knew a thing or two about dealers and their sale-room tricks. He guessed that his hidden opponent would recognize his little try-on for what it was; and he was right; there was no change in the speed of the bidding from the cubby-hole. It now raced ahead again, five pounds advance each time, coming to Willy at 'A hundred and seventy-five'.

'Hundred and eighty.'

Willy nodded again. 'Hundred and eighty-five. Hundred and eighty-five pounds bid.'

'Hey, steady on, Willy.' It was Ropey whispering. 'Don't get landed with it. It was "there" a moment ago—let the b——r have it.'

'Hundred and ninety.'

Again Willy nodded. 'Hundred and ninety-five.'

'Hundred and ninety-five—two hundred. Two hundred pounds bid. Two hundred pounds . . .'

Willy lost his pluck and with a small sigh of nervous relief shook his head, telling the auctioneer he had finished. He would dearly have loved to slam the bidding well into the two hundreds. Inwardly he was sure that his opponent was good for another fifty pounds but in this instance, as others were concerned in it, better to be safe than sorry.

The auctioneer was still calling for another advance, but the battle was over, the hammer descended and the buyer was named—in a quiet voice not audible above the general hubbub which broke out from an audience let loose from a tense, enforced silence.

At the back a certain amount of tee-hee-heeing was already taking place.

'He's got that one round his neck, haw, haw!'

'That'll learn him. Let's see him write an article on that one—just about cooked his goose.'

'Ssh! Now look, chaps. Be sensible!' It was Reg speaking. 'Don't go shooting your mouths off about this yet. Remember, he will be paying by cheque, and cheques can be stopped. Better wait until old Prater gets the cheque and we get it cashed. One or other of us will have to pay it through our accounts. Take a good week to sort it all out, so mind now— no one breathes a word until we have the money. If anyone does they will be out of all future settlements.'

Oaths of assurances varying in depth and colour were given, and out into the fresh air trooped the dealers, well satisfied with the morning's work.

Up on the rostrum Hickory, the auctioneer, was proceeding with the sale, a slight smirk of satisfaction on his face. He had hoped that this table would bring more than two hundred pounds, but that was quite a satisfactory sum, representing some thirty-five pounds commission. He was very pleased the antique trade had been outbid. Nothing pleased him more.

Just down below him and a little to his left was a gentleman well satisfied, already planning to take a fine and rare piece of Chippendale furniture up to his London flat, where he could show and boast about it to his friends. He had been prepared to pay more than two hundred— much more—but then these local country dealers did not really know or understand the value of fine furniture. It was just a matter of luck that no good London dealer had put in an appearance—bad advertising on the part of the auctioneer. He decided to remain where he was until the half-hour break for lunch at twelve-thirty, when he would pay for his table and request special permission to take it away before it could be deliberately or accidentally damaged during the afternoon session.

Out in the yard calculations were being made. After paying Bert Hammond his seventy-five pounds, the auctioneer's commission, etc., the seven men who had been in on the deal collected twelve pounds each —very little, thought Willy, for all his trouble. Still, it had been worth it to slam down the unmentionable Starling!

9   On the Tap

Ethel's hot-water bottle leaked in the night, or rather the early hours of the morning. The bed had to be stripped and the only thing left to do was to get up and dress.

'All your fault. How could any bottle stand up to your great fat rump?'

Tempers were frayed over breakfast and Willy decided to get out of the way. He had no idea what he was going to do. The only sale was at Riverbridge, twenty-five miles away, and having heard from Peter Nebbing that there were only two lots—a toilet mirror with a broken upright and a butler's tray—decided that there would be enough 'boys' from nearby Lidmoor to eat both lots.

Everyone has got a butler's tray reckoned up, he decided, even the auctioneers. Won't be bought under the hammer for less than a fiver. The mirror?—not more than six or seven pounds to be shared out between a minimum of ten dealers. Definitely not worth going that far for fifteen shillings. Wonder if Tom's got anything fresh? Shouldn't think so—only saw him the day before yesterday.

The prosperous-looking Cadillac rolled out from the yard, past Ethel's spring garden with daffodils in the fresh uncut grass under young apple trees, into the road. To the right lay Torminster, with Tom Elliot en route, to the left open country and the moors in the distance. It was an early April day, as warm as summer might be in a sharper climate, with a clear blue sky and small white clouds that briefly shadowed the tumbling chequer-patterned fields on the moorland slopes.

I'll go 'on the tap' again, said Willy to himself, sniffing all the smells of spring as he stuck his head out of the window. Haven't 'tapped' for years. See if I can still do it. Might earn myself a crust of bread. Must make sure I've got some other dealer's card to show. He felt in the front pigeon-hole and picked out Fred Mellis's trade card.

To go 'on the tap', or 'tapping' as it is generally known to the antique trade, means exactly what it implies—tapping on the doors of suitable-looking houses with a view to getting in to buy antiques. It is one of the hardest but most remunerative ways of finding antiques. No self-respecting dealer would contemplate doing it, some going to the length of refusing to deal in goods so acquired. This is quite understandable. An antique dealer of repute, with a jealous regard of his good name, would naturally wish to avoid the rows and unpleasantness which often arise when goods which have been 'tapped' are displayed for sale in someone's shop.

The hereditary instincts of a succession of Irish cattle-dealing ancestors handed on to him in what little Irish blood he still possessed made Willy a born 'tapper'. His manner could be very pleasant and in-gratiating when he wanted and this, combined with a full smile showing a perfect set of teeth—his own—making him look the picture of inno-cence, could often work wonders on the unsuspecting.

Ahead lay the moors and over on the other side a vast territory radiating out from the focal hub of Bosmouth. Bosmouth had been a seaport for centuries, and prosperity had spread out like a fan throughout the surrounding countryside. Although frequently combed, this area was still rich in antiquities. Great estates and dwellings had come and gone, providing quite a happy hunting ground for an industrious tapper. Willy felt industrious that morning. If I can cop a good lot, he said to himself, thinking of Ethel and her hot-water bottle, the promise of a new dress and a trip up to London might smooth over this morning's incident.

The miles slipped away under the bonnet of his shining vehicle as he roared up between high, red, twisting banks splashed with primroses, running with rivulets hurrying to join brown foaming streams, dappled with sunlight and the shadows of branches lightly in leaf. Before long he was flying over the brown moors, miles of them, with patches of emerald in the hollows and a patch or two of snow where the sun did not reach. On the other side the country lay at his feet; he knew it like the back of his hand and had already picked his district. No good going where one has been before—might knock on the same door and be remembered. I've had some of that. Never forget what the old spike-nosed woman had to say to me. I'll try Littleton. Must be sixteen years ago since I went there. Thirty-five miles from home and far enough away for me to be unknown.

The art of 'tapping' was to find the right kind of house, occupied by the right type of person. As Willy approached Littleton—almost large enough to be called a small country town—he came to a village whose name he did not know. Reducing speed to fifteen miles per hour, he let his eyes roam on either side and as he passed each successive house his mind worked overtime with a mixture of instinctive perception and experienced assessment. Small cottage—workman—recently done up—tidy inside—new furniture—hire purchase probably—nothing there. Same again—new house—recently built—might be an antique or two worked into a modern scheme of decoration—wouldn't want to sell. Another workman's cottage—bad state—might be an oak chest—probably not there—waste of time—old woman want to jaw half the morning away. Another field—house over there on the right—possible—know in a second or two—looks interesting—standing well back—not all that big—Victorian—big hedges not well kept—slow down—garden very dilapidated—pull up a few yards beyond gate. House trying to look respectable but slowly failing. Get out and go in. Just at that moment Willy saw the Church.

'Bally parson's house—waste of time!'

By and large, parsons and doctors were the antique dealer's worst enemies, or so Willy thought. Nearly every house in their parish or practice was open to them. Most of them were well up in antiques and current market values—some of them were downright knowledgeable on the subject, even to the point of being serious collectors. Doctors were the worst of the two. The National Health Service had somewhat curbed the activities of the local country practitioner; he was better off than before, with his monthly cheque and expenses. But as his patients no

longer had to pay, apart from an ever-increasing contribution by way
of the weekly Insurance stamp, he had no chance to run up a fat bill by
unnecessary visits just because there happened to be a decent mahogany
bowfronted chest of drawers upstairs in the bedroom.

'Don't fret yourself, Spencer, I know how difficult times are. Only
sent the bill in as a matter of routine. Take your time—need not even
pay it in cash if you don't want. There's a chest of drawers I happened
to see in your back bedroom. . . .'

One thing could be said in the doctor's favour. He did at least give a
service measurable to some extent in terms of money—whether the
service was anything like equal to the market value of the goods that
changed hands was a matter for speculation.

Of parsons Willy took an even more jaundiced view. Either they had
fat livings and lived in whacking great Queen Anne rectories stuffed with
furniture to match, and sent you away with a flea in your ear; or they
were as poor as the proverbial church mice and lived in whacking great
rectories without two sticks to rub together. Once or twice he had had a
lucky deal with the in-between group—a country rector who'd inherited
a piece or two, or wormed them out of some elderly spinster with constant
flattery—got her to remember him in her will.

All this passed through Willy's mind as he regarded the house from
the bottom of the drive. It was a large rectory, and a look at the weeds, the
shaggy lawns, and the general air of slow decay was enough for him. Not
a sausage worth having there—sold it long ago if they ever had it. Won't
bother to go up and try.

With all his wits razor-edge sharp and now properly in the 'tapping'
mood he climbed back into his estate car and started up the engine.

At the cross-roads just beyond the Church he hesitated. There was
the biggest part of the village to the left and right, but as his main objective
was Littleton he decided to carry straight on. Some distance along the
road he tried two possibles but could get no response to his knocking
from either, although he was certain that a curtain was pulled back in one
of the upstairs windows

Trouble with all these murders in the papers is that people won't open
their doors to honest men.

On the outskirts of the village he had a go at a large Edwardian-
looking house. The path to the front door led past the drawing-room—
nicely furnished—satinwood—looks genuine period—good stuff—
might be able to pick up an odd lot. Pressing the bell very gently he heard

it sound somewhere in the depths of the house. The door was quite quickly opened by a tweedy-dressed lady, middle fifties.

'Good morning, madam,' began Willy, politely raising his hat and producing a pleasant smile. 'May I proffer my card as an introduction? I am buying certain types of antiques for the export market and I was wond——'

Slam!

He had the door shut in his face quite often, used to it in fact, but seldom so quickly and with such force. Card in hand he reeled back off the step.

'Ill-mannered bitch!' he muttered, walking steadily back down the drive, knowing full well that a pair of gimlet eyes were boring into his back from one or other of the windows. It was as much as he could do to stop himself from turning round and giving her 'the bird'. However, a wealthy man who is a good buyer of export antiques must always keep his dignity.

He left the gate open, with the fervent hope that a herd of cows coming up the road would find their way in. With ears still singing he got back in his car. Nearly into the next village he pulled up sharply. On the right side of the road was a house—a 'tapper's' must—not large, but long, low, and rambling.

H'm, could have been a farmhouse at one time, he reckoned. Had a lot spent on it over the last few years—just look at the gardens—magnificent —somebody here is keen on gardening, or was—those shrubs are too thick—should have been thinned—lawn edges untidy and weeds sprout-ing on the gravel drive—retired civil servant.

He parked his car a few yards along the road, got out and started up the drive.

House painted about four years ago—could do with another coat. Some money spent here all right. Look at that garage—thatch on it and all to match the house.

His retired civil servant guess was almost a bull's-eye. It had been the home of a retired manager of a large bank.

He knocked once on a fine, highly polished brass door-knocker—a laughing sun with curly rays all round. Difficult things to buy from off front doors. Bet I don't buy it. Rare type—worth a tenner.

The door was presently opened by an elderly, mild-looking lady— Looks worried or harassed—not well or not sleeping—rings under her eyes.

H

'Good morning, madam,' he began once again. 'I am buying certain types of antiques for the export market, and was wondering if you had anything you would care to sell?'

Having got all this out without interruption, Willy handed over Fred Mellis's trade card.

'I do not normally travel round in this way for, as you can see, I have an established business, but I have taken on a very large export order— the United States of course—and not being able to find all I want in my own locality just have to tour the country in order to fulfil it. I am paying very good prices for certain items—much higher than average—bacon dishes—pairs of overlay glass vases, Burmese glass, cameo glass, coloured Wedgwood—oh, dozens of items, madam.'

During these last few moments each had been carefully studying the other. Unknown to Willy, his arrival was quite opportune.

Six years previously Robert Hemmington and his wife Joan had bought their way into this lovely old bit of country. The rambling cottage had not been in very good order then, and nearly three thousand pounds had been spent on converting, modernization, and general repairs and decorations. Six happy years they spent, keen gardeners both, the result being one of the finest small landscape gardens for miles around. Robert received a good pension, had made quite a number of profitable speculations during the years he had been District Manager, things were comfortable and life was good.

One afternoon in November of the previous year Robert Hemmington had been removing the last row of runner-bean sticks in the kitchen garden behind the house. For a second he paused, turned slowly, stepped off the garden and even more slowly walked up the path towards the house. He went straight through the kitchen into the sitting-room, forgetting to change his gardening shoes—a thing he had never forgotten to do before. Upstairs his wife thought: Gracious, he has come in early for his tea. I haven't even cut the bread and butter yet. When she found him he was unconscious, and within ten minutes he was dead.

The winter that followed had been a hard one for Mrs Hemmington —the loneliness, the responsibility of the house, all the bills and payments which previously her husband had attended to. She missed him terribly, and also the pension which had ceased on his death. She was by no means poor, but gradually she had come to realize that she could no longer afford to live here in this lovely house, what with the rates, fuel bills, and three pounds a week for a jobbing gardener to keep the gardens up to a reasonable standard. That very afternoon she had intended going into Bosmouth to see an estate agent about putting her house on the market. Here on her doorstep was a man who wanted to buy antiques. She could do with some ready money. He looks honest and nice enough, she decided. His suit, if a little loud in pattern, is nicely tailored. Clean shirt and collar. His car looks like an American one—perhaps that accounts for his suits—he's probably connected with American business. I think I'll ask him in.

Meanwhile, Willy had had a careful look at Mrs Hemmington. Dressed in black—widow—looks pale—had a bad time of it. Might be a bit hard up—perhaps not, judging by the look of all the money splashed around —some goods here, too.

Willy's eyes had slipped past Mrs Hemmington to a fine Hepplewhite period side-table standing in the hall.

Good clean lot—mahogany—three drawers with original handles —square taper legs and spade feet—much better than turned legs— could give fifty quid to earn a tenner profit.

'What did you say you wanted to buy?'

'Anything well over a hundred years old—silver, Sheffield plate, mahogany furniture if of good quality—china, glass, anything, madam.'

'Please come in.'

'Thank you, madam.'

The battle was already half won.

He was ushered into the sitting-room, noting as he went a very fine pair of Regency black-and-gold-framed mirrors with black-and-white Wedgwood plaques in the classical style set in the cornice of each—a rare pair. On the far side of the hall was a thick-legged Victorian buffet. Not much idea here, he thought, but his eye did not miss what appeared to be a good silver salver on the bottom tier of the buffet.

The sitting-room was a large room with furnishings of good quality but humble-jumbled regarding position and period. Edwardian, Georgian, and Victorian—all, to his connoisseur's eye, jostled and shrieked at one another. There, undoubtedly, was the best piece—a little gem of a mahogany bureau, Chippendale period, made about 1765 and only two feet six inches wide. The handles were original, he could tell that by the patina round them. The colour and grain of the carefully chosen veneers were superb. Good dealer could get the odds over a hundred and twenty for that, if he had the right customer. Seventy-five is the giving price, subject to a careful examination.

'How much do you want for the bureau over there?'

'Mr Mellis, that is the only piece I am definitely not going to sell. It was my husband's—his favourite piece, and also a family heirloom. Most of the antiques here are family belongings but I must dispose of quite a number of them as my sister's house, where I am going, is already quite full and I will only be able to take a few things. I am afraid I don't know what they are all worth—not all of them. I leave it to you to make your best offer for what you want and then I can consider it. The contents were valued altogether with the house for death duties but the solicitor attended to all that. However, I do know what figure my husband valued his bureau at.'

'I would very much like to buy it, madam. Perhaps I can tempt you into selling it?'

'No. Definitely not. I am taking it with me to London.'

This was what Willy had been angling and waiting for. She did not know much about most of the stuff by the sound of it, but she did have an idea about the bureau and it was certain she didn't intend to part with it.

'I will give you three hundred and fifty pounds for it,' he said very quietly.

He saw Mrs Hemmington start. Her husband had, in recent years, told her it was worth about a hundred pounds.

'I really can't bring myself to sell it, Mr Mellis, but I am sure you have made a good offer for it.'

'I have, madam. I always do for what I want.'

He followed up the crafty move of offering a high price for something not likely to be sold to him by another one. He produced his 'flash'—a wad of five-pound notes held together by an elastic band. His was a genuine roll but most 'tappers' had a trick of having about eighty to a hundred genuine five-pound notes on the outside of their wad, with sheets of toilet paper sandwiched in between, giving the appearance of almost uncountable wealth.

'I pay cash for everything.'

He was now well established, having proved that he paid good prices. Had she accepted his offer it would have been quite easy to wriggle out of it at the end of the deal by saying that he would have to bring his customer along to see it before he finally paid for it. He had produced his 'flash', giving her the confidence that he was going to pay up on the spot. Also, the very sight of all those five-pound notes had produced its own peculiar psychological effect. Above all, he had 'killed the bureau stone dead'. He could not buy it but by his offer of three hundred and fifty pounds he had ensured that no other dealer could buy it in the future. Human nature would not part with a bureau for seventy-five—even a hundred—pounds, when three hundred and fifty had once been offered for it.

A chuckle came at the thought of any other dealer attempting to buy the bureau. Get a right good flea in his ear and be shown the door straight away! Now down to business!

'There are a pair of fire-screens in the fireplace. May I examine them? Thank you.' Hepplewhite—about 1780—very dainty—original needle-work—one foot repaired—been ironed up underneath—pity, but it often happens. Nice pair—right as the bank. Worth forty nicker for the two.

'A great pity about this damage, madam. My clients are very fussy. They expect everything to be perfect. It is a silly attitude. How can anything a hundred and fifty years old be expected to be perfect? How-ever, one's customers are always right. They'll just have to put up with the broken leg—there, do you see where it has been repaired? Pity. It affects the value. I can allow you fifteen pounds for the pair—twenty-five had they been absolutely perfect.'

'Yes. Thank you. They aren't on my list to take with me, so you can have them.'

'Thank you, madam. What is next?'

'How about the china-cabinet over there? I am not taking that with me.'

'Too late for me. Could not export it. Importer would be required to pay duty on it.'

He hardly gave a glance at the late Victorian china-cabinet indicated by Mrs Hemmington. But inside it, though . . .

'May I take a look at some of the china inside the cabinet?'

He had spotted a fine jug of Swansea shape, decorated with silver resist lustre on a canary-yellow background, with reserved panels in white decorated with bullfinches. (Bet the blooming thing's cracked. One like that would be! Anything decent always is.)

'Yes, do so by all means. The key is there in the lock.'

Willy pulled out two white Worcester vases, marked with the 1851 mark—studied them carefully, found a crack in one, shook his head and put them back. He had no interest in them anyway, but had to work up to that jug gradually. He examined some trashy figures, then picked out the jug.

'Not bad—nice jug.'

Careful, lad, he told himself, his eyes intent on every detail, the money's here if it isn't cracked—can't see one—looks all right. Handle looks sound—give it a tap. H'm—not much of a ring, but you never do get it from pottery—didn't go 'thud' anyway. What the devil is it worth? A small one with a slight rim crack fetched forty pounds last year and that one hadn't panels of bird decoration.

'Good design and colour, madam. People like that sort of thing. Always popular. What have I got to give you for it?'

'My husband said it was Swansea. He thought it might be worth as much as twenty pounds.'

'Probably, probably, but that would be to a private buyer, and a good one at that. One has to make a profit. I think fifteen pounds would be fair. Most other dealers would try to buy it for ten or less.'

'Put it down on your list. I will accept the fifteen pounds, only do make sure it is in good condition.'

Down it went on Willy's list—yellow jug, fifteen pounds—and so on, till they were in the dining-room. Here a pair of eighteenth-century Adam's design Sheffield-plated candelabra went down at sixteen pounds, he having declared them to be 'electro-plate and the copper showing through as well—poor condition', breathing on them to prove his point about the electro-plate and age. Poor Mrs Hemmington could not really follow what he meant, but coming from a man who seemed to know so much, she took his word for it.

Those candelabra were worth a good fifty pounds.

It was in the dining-room that Willy displayed the fine points which go to make a top-class 'tapper'. On the sideboard, between the pair of candelabra he had already bought, was a large mahogany tea-caddy standing on four ball-turned feet. It was late Regency, about 1830, big, heavy, and clumsy-looking. Willy lifted the lid and there were the usual two covered compartments with the glass mixing-bowl in between. This type of tea-caddy was seldom bought by the trade, but antique dealers with shops usually managed to push them on to those Americans whose taste matched their knowledge as suitable souvenirs of old England. These caddies were invariably guaranteed as 'Regency', with a date of '*circa* 1820', to ensure a Customs duty-free passage into America. They were always regarded as 'stickers'—being slow to sell. Willy did not want it.

'How about the tea-caddy? My husband was always fond of it. It came from his family. He could remember his grandmother using it.'

Willy hesitated, turning the caddy over to inspect the condition. See these things everywhere. No blinking good at all. Don't want it—never get more than twenty-five bob for them. Usually priced about three pounds ten when offered for sale. Expect she has seen one or two like this in the shops.

He pulled out the two separate sliding compartments and looked inside. Once he had found a maker's label in a tea-caddy; antique pieces of furniture with their original maker's label are quite rare and the label adds considerably to the value. Needless to say, Willy did not leave the label in his tea-caddy but steamed it off and stuck it carefully on to the back of a drawer of a much more important piece of furniture.

'Seven pounds for this tea-caddy. That is more than I usually pay, but it is in very nice condition.'

Mrs Hemmington was delighted. Only the week before she had seen a very similar tea-caddy displayed in a Bosmouth shop-window, priced at four pounds.

He really is giving good prices, she thought.

She nodded, and down it went on the list, tea-caddy—seven pounds. Willy knew that he could well afford the certain loss of five pounds which he was going to make on that one.

'What about the sideboard? I know it's a little on the large side but it's in beautiful condition.'

'Cannot move oak at all. Just will not sell over in America. They burnt their fingers so badly with all the dud oak that was sent over in between the two wars that they want to forget all about it. I could tell you some stories, madam. The one I always liked the most was about the very wealthy American who was sold a dud oak chair by quite a respectable dealer. It was carved on the back as well as the front. From that moment onwards this American would not buy a chair unless it was carved on the back as well—he soon had hundreds!'

Mrs Hemmington laughed.

'Mind you, I can always do with small pieces of antique oak for the home market, but not that sideboard—much too big.'

On the same wall was a bow-fronted chest of drawers functioning as a serving-table. It looked out of place because all the other dining-room furniture was oak of various periods, much to Willy's sour disappointment. He steeled himself against the mahogany chest of drawers: Large one, but not too big, about three foot six wide, I suppose—good fat belly on it and cross-banded top—two nice features. The splayed feet and curved apron underneath are nicely proportioned too. Worth thirty-five quid to sell in a shop. Couldn't get any more than twenty-nine from the trade. Have to give her twenty-five quid to keep my end up. Wouldn't see a fiver profit. No! Damned if I'm going to hump that thing about for four quid, especially when I've done so well already.

'Pity about that,' indicating the bow-front chest. 'I'm overstocked with that type. They sell, but not so quickly as they used. It's a nice one but I am afraid I am forced to leave it. I would like to buy the mirror hanging on the wall above it.'

'I did think about taking it with me.'

'Ten pounds for it. How's that?'

Mrs. Hemmington hesitated. Ten pounds did not seem much of a price. It was a very nice-looking mirror and came from her husband's side of the family. Her sister only wanted her to bring things from their own side, but she liked the mirror.

'That doesn't seem to be much for a nice mirror like that. I know it is an old one.'

'It's only a small one. With mirrors, the bigger the better, up to a certain size—huge ones will not sell nowadays. Eleven pounds ten, then,' said Willy, trying to look hurt and hard done by. He bought it.

The bedrooms were furnished with 'modern', to his disappointment. Not a sausage upstairs for him.

He had got sixteen things on his list, all small and easily transportable, and all worth far more than he had given.

Out in the hall he had a go at the silver salver, but without success. After a long struggle with herself, Mrs Hemmington parted with the pair of Regency mirrors for sixty pounds, saying 'no' to Willy's query about the Hepplewhite period side-table. The sixty pounds for the mirrors was the nearest thing to being a decent offer in the whole of Willy's purchases—a total of one hundred and eighty-two pounds.

Slowly he counted out the notes—thirty-six fivers and two grubby 'ones' from a roll kept lose in his pocket. He shook his head when asked if he wanted a receipt.

'You have the money and I have the goods—you realize that I must take them with me? I shan't be this way again for a considerable time and I don't trust carriers overmuch—something always gets broken.'

'Oh yes, of course. I'm sure there will be some dust behind the things —especially those mirrors. I will get a duster.'

Her pocket was burning with the five-pound notes. In her mind all the bills were paid and plenty left besides.

Willy made several trips up and down the drive, refusing all offers of assistance. He had no wish to bring the car up the drive to the house. Loading did not take him long. He had plenty of wrappers and all the things were small. The mirrors he placed back to back and stood on end, padded round with wrappers and other pieces to keep them in position. They had to be looked after.

Back in the hall he had one more go at the Hepplewhite side-table. He did not like leaving it behind but could not very well offer a substantial increase to tempt her into selling without making his first offer look mean.

'I will think it over and let you know,' said Mrs Hemmington. 'Thank you so much. I am sure all this has been much better for me than sending my things to the sale-rooms, although quite a number of things will have to go there—all the bedroom furniture. One never seems to get very much for things at sales.'

'It has been nice meeting you, madam, and it has been a pleasure to do business with you.'

They shook hands—all smiles.

On his way back down the drive he thought: By all the Saints, what a haul! Straight back home for me—no use going on—won't repeat this again in a hurry. Those mirrors! That jug!

He wisely went on to Littleton in order to make a circular route for home, his car laden with a certain three hundred pounds profit.

Just think of old Fred Mellis! Pity I lost that table in the hall, it was a good lot. If she writes and says I can have it old Fred will get the letter. If he goes down there I bet he goes a purler on that bureau. Good luck to him!

There was a sequel to the story. Not long after Fred Mellis himself came into Willy's showrooms. He began looking around, but Willy could see his heart wasn't in it.

'Anything wrong, Fred? What are you up to down here anyway? There's nothing on as far as I know.'

That did it. Fred could contain himself no longer.

'What am I up to? Me? I come down a hundred and seventy-odd

miles to get a door shut in my face—*and* she wrote to me too—that's the stinging part of it. Here it is.' And he slapped down a letter in feminine handwriting. It was from Mrs Hemmington. '. . . In view of the fact that I shall be unable to accommodate the small Hepplewhite side-table in my sister's house you can have it for the price you offered.'

'Well, well,' said Willy. 'And so—? Listen, old boy, come into the lounge and have a drink.'

It was a long and, to Willy, an increasingly entertaining story. Fred, of course, couldn't make sense of the letter; but a Hepplewhite side-table is a Hepplewhite side-table so he had gone down to investigate—she'd said in her letter that the telephone had been cut off as she was moving almost at once.

'I think there must be some mistake,' she'd said on seeing Fred at the door. But he succeeded in proving his credentials and she let him in, and there was the side-table.

'A good little lot. Worth fifty-five nicker easy. "And what was I supposed to have offered for it, madam?" "The other gentleman offered thirty pounds for it." "That's all right with me, madam," I said, "I'll give you that price for it." There was no need to look at the flaming thing twice. It was a real clean genuine lot. See? Just then I spot the sweetest little mahogany bureau you ever did see—over in the corner it was. See? Lovely little job—not in the "fine" category but very, very nice. Good colour, right period, tiny too—one of the smallest of its type I've seen— wasn't any more than two-eight wide. I said: "I would like to buy the bureau there, madam." "Oh, would you?" she says in a funny sort of voice. "And what would you offer for it?" I get over to it, turn it inside out—can't fault it anywhere. That size and colour you could go the whole hog. See? On my reckoning, worth between a hundred and a hundred and twenty to sell. At first I thought about offering her sixty nicker for it, but it was obvious someone or other had been in the house pricing goods, so I offered her eighty-five quid for it. See? Which was a jolly good price. She rounds on me like a wildcat. I couldn't follow all she said—or shouted, rather. Couldn't get a word in edgeways. She was letting rip like a waterfall. "I knew there was something wrong the moment I saw you," she says. "Coming here trying to rob decent people." Rogue, thief, cheat—I was called the blooming lot. She told me to get out. I demanded an explanation. "Explanation!" she says. "It's you who should be called upon to give an explanation! Daring to offer me eighty-five pounds for a valuable antique worth hundreds." It wasn't any good trying to argue with her—the woman was "bats"—kept pushing me towards the door, shouting and hollering all the time about sending for the police if I didn't leave at once. I tell you, I've never had anything like that happen to me before in the whole of my life. Me—Fred Mellis! I turned round and went out through the front door, with her right behind me all the way carrying on something proper. It was no good trying to say anything to her—the woman was crazy. Didn't she bang that door on me, too! I've never been treated like that before and I'm not going to take it lying down, either. See?'

Fred's voice tailed off into falsetto.

Poor old Fred, thought Willy. He's taking it bad.

'Better have another drink, Fred. Don't take it to heart. A mistake has been made somewhere.'

'Think I don't know that? Coming back from there to your place I've tried to sort it out. The only thing I can think of is that some blooming tapper got in there on the strength of one of my cards. I've got a good mind to go back to that woman and sort it out properly—shouting or no shouting. See?'

'Drink up, Fred,' was Willy's only comment.

10 The Silver Salt-shaker

Wednesday was always a busy day. In the country very few sales are ever held on a Monday or Tuesday, except perhaps when a four- or five-day sale is in progress. They are frequently held on Wednesdays, but the most popular days are always Thursdays and Fridays. Why? Impossible to answer. Established custom with auctioneering firms, perhaps—firms which are too busy selling livestock in the markets on the usual Tuesday market day to be able to cope with a furniture sale at the same time.

This Wednesday, a close, rainy day towards the end of May, was a scramble, one sale taking place over at Cuddlington and three sales to be viewed for the selling on the following day: two small ones and one with a catalogue giving descriptions sufficient to bring the whole of the London trade down. There was another sale taking place on Friday. All these had to be 'done', starting with the sale at Cuddlington, no catalogue available, and the place mid-way between all the other places so that ground had to be covered twice, and hilly ground at that—over some of the wildest moorland in the West Country. A rough calculation gave at least two hundred and twenty miles travelling.

Willy also had a large consignment of goods to be labelled and got ready for the carriers who were calling to collect for delivery to a shipping agent in London. After a hurried attention to his export order Willy gobbled down an untasted breakfast and set out for Cuddlington. He had only a vague idea, given him by Tom, as to where the sale was taking place. He stopped in the village to ask the first local inhabitant he came across.

'Zale? Thur bain't no zale on 'ere todoy. Twer won laast wick doän tuther zide o' Bidderide. Manur 'Ouze Varm? Oi knows thur bain't no zale on thur coz oi do work thur, zee? Tuk th'r marnin' offen vor ter cum doän an' zee the doctur. Me rheumatics iz bad, zee? Th' mizzuz said: "Fred, iffen thee dursn't goo down an' zee th' doctur, hi'll 'av un cum up an' zee thee 'ere in bed." That wur enuff fur oi. Oi zez ter 'er: "Lak now, Bess, iffen thee—" '

'Good morning,' said Willy, letting in his clutch. The old man jumped back as the car shot forward and stood in the middle of the road staring after it.

Should have known better than to stop to ask that fellow anything! Looked half daft the moment I set eyes on him. Ah, there's the Post Office!

The postmistress was more helpful.

'The only Manor House Farm here in Cuddlington is owned by the Braebrackers and there certainly isn't a sale there. Are you sure you don't mean Caddington? That's twelve miles from here on the Tilltown road.'

Cuddlington? Caddington? Perhaps Tom had made a mistake. The sale must be in Caddington.

Willy wrote down the directions, bought a pound of eating apples, and set out for Caddington. He found it at the second attempt, found the Manor House Farm, and the sale about to begin. He got a catalogue from the porter and pushed his way through the various rooms. The contents were surprisingly bad compared with the beauty and the size of the house. There were three good lots. A pair of seventeenth-century two-tiered brass chandeliers, recently wired and adapted for electricity—a very good pair, not too big, and with an unusual geometrical design. Pairs of chandeliers are rare. They were in the dining-room, and were listed as Lot No. 7. Lot 148 was a magnificent Coalport dessert service, with eight of the fifteen plates cracked, one *sucrier* cracked and minus cover and stand, the other minus cover, two of the eight dishes cracked and riveted, and two of the remaining six had been put in the oven at some time or another—baked to a dirty brown. Willy swore to himself as he came across each damaged piece. Had the whole lot been in perfect condition it would have been worth a good two hundred pounds. Early-nineteenth-century porcelain at its finest, not even a half-set could be made up out of all the pieces. It was still worth quite a bit of money to sell separately. The apple-green background, the rich gilding, and the superbly painted bouquets of flowers in the reserve panels, made each separate piece worthy of a place in any china-collector's cabinet.

The third lot was a silver Queen Anne period kitchen salt-shaker— crude-looking thing, four inches high, perfectly plain, straight cylindrical sides, plain domed top with holes pierced in a haphazard pattern, a thin flat handle on one side, soldered just underneath the lid and again about halfway down the side of the body, the end of the flat handle being turned outwards and upwards in a curl. The marks stamped on the underside of the base were well rubbed but visible on a close examination —maker's mark, duty mark, London Town hall-mark, and the date letter. A very rare piece, worth far more than it looked. Unfortunately the salt-shaker was among a lot of odds and ends displayed in the kitchen quarters and due to be sold nearly at the end of the sale.

Willy was in a quandary. Should he stay on and wait till the end, or go on to the other sales? The three main lots here were worth having, together with three papier-mâché trays, a butler's tray, two copper coal-scuttles, and a few other nondescript things which, if bought at the right price, could all earn money. Quite a crowd was milling round, but judging by the look of the people there would be no major opposition— with luck. Willy decided to take a chance of being able to view the other sales later on. He carefully hid the salt-shaker at the bottom of the lot of oddments in which it was included. The auctioneer now made his appearance, but still not another dealer. Willy went outside and stood in the porch, drawing in a few last breaths of sweet fresh air before going back in for the 'scrum down'.

'Anything here?'

He jumped and turned round to see Tom and Reg Bardon. Bobbie Trewen, Hamish Jarwell from Overmoor, Peter Nebbing and Uncle Tom Cobleigh and all were coming up the drive! His hope of getting a good day's work faded.

'Only two lots any good; the best one is round in the stables at the back of the house. Jolly fine lot it is, too. Can't begin to reckon it. S'cuse me a minute, I want to make myself comfortable before the sale starts.'

As his friends trooped round in the direction of the stables, indicated by a vague wave of his hand, Willy stepped inside and grabbed the porter.

'Quick—you know me?—Shaun from Torminster. There's a pound

note. Buy that pair of brass chandeliers for me—Lot 7. Go up to sixty-five pounds, only have them put down in your name. If you buy them cheap you won't lose by it. If anybody wants to know—you bought them for a private gentleman.'

The porter nodded, the pound note disappeared like magic, and Willy hurried outside to the sheds and stables, and met Tom and Peter.

'Where's the good lot which is supposed to be out here?'

'It's in the stables—next door down.'

'We've been in there. Can't see anything except some saddles, troughs, scythes, and things. Reg is still in there.'

'A sundial's hung up on the wall. Big brass one, very dirty, just inside the door.'

'Well, we didn't see it.'

'Let me get in and show you. Look! Here it is, just inside the door, hung up on the nail with—well, I'll be——It's gone! You don't mean to say someone's half-inched it already? That's where it was—hanging up with all those horseshoes and chains—Lot 487. Five sets of shoes and sundry items. Well, what do you know about that? Come on, Reg, what have you done with it? You lot have hidden it somewhere.'

'That's a fact we haven't. None of us have set eyes on it.'

You are right there, laughed Willy to himself, neither have I for that matter. Wonder if they have sold Lot 7 yet? . . . 'We'll have to make some enquiries—can't let some light-fingered so-and-so get away with that. It was a good sundial. I think we had better hurry up and get back inside the house—good pair of brass chandeliers coming up early in the sale—don't want to miss them.'

This information started a scramble, his colleagues realizing what time they had been wasting.

Willy caught up with Tom.

'Hey, Tom, not so fast. Getting in there won't do you any good. The chandeliers will have been sold by now. One good turn deserves another. Thank you very much for sending that American dealer to me last night.'

'Did he come out to you? Good. I had a fair deal with him. He's a goer. Wanted to know if there was anybody else he could call on near by. He had done all the other shops in the town. Reg had a good deal with him. I gave him your address and told him the evening would be the best time to find you at home.'

'That was decent of you, Tom. I had a "cracker" with him. Mind you, the bloke knew his onions and knew what he wanted. I think he was the first Yankee dealer I have ever had who didn't argue over the price. He either bought at the quoted price or he didn't. Wouldn't go back to a lot he had said no to, either. I soon got the hang of him and after one or two refusals started quoting rock-bottom prices straight away, not sticking a pound or two on just to knock it off. My stock had piled up a bit and I was pleased to unload a few things. Wonderful feeling when you are taking something like a hundred pounds a minute. Did you see his invoice book? I reckon he has spent something over two hundred thousand pounds this trip. I took nearly two thousand from him and my invoice number was nine hundred and twenty-seven. Fred told me on the blower that he had nearly sold out to a Yank. Wonder if it was the same chap?'

'Probably is. I didn't do anything like you did with him—just over three hundred. He has been touring the country dealers—couldn't buy much up in London because of the prices they ask up there. They are slowly committing suicide, he thinks. You know, Willy, I've got a good mind to give up my shop and go in for it the way you do. It's a pleasure to sell to the export market. They know what they want and buy it if you've got it. You sell them the goods and apart from fixing labels, packing the odd lot of china, etc., arranging for it to be sent to the shipping agents carriage forward, the business is finished. You sell the lot as it stands, and if a piece of furniture happens to have a few worm-holes you didn't spot you don't get a customer insisting that you take it back.'

'You'll have to make up your own mind on that, Tom, regarding doing things my way. As you know, I sell entirely to the trade, home as well as overseas—business is good—wonderful, but for all your trials and troubles your kind of business is much safer. If a quiet time ever comes—as it well may—I will be really quiet—jolly near dead, but at least you will be able to sell a few thirty-bob lots to someone or other, just to keep the pot boiling.

'Let's get back into the house to see how the sale is getting on. By the way—the sundial supposed to be in the stable doesn't exist. It was just my idea to get the crowd out of the way while the chandeliers were being sold. I didn't dare give you the wink. I covered them well— gave one of the porters a quid to buy them. If I haven't got them no one else will get a bargain. You find out from the porter with the moustache if he has bought them. I don't want to be seen near him for the rest of the sale. Peter has eyes at the back of his head for spotting anything going on. There are only two more lots any good. A dessert service and a bit of silver hidden in an odd lot in the kitchen—a copper coal-scuttle or two, butler's tray, and the odd bit of papier mâché. Keep it up about the sundial, mind.'

The selling was still going on in the dining-room.

'What lot are they on, Reg?'

'Lot 38.'

'Crumbs, he's got a move on. Which of you bought the chandeliers?' Willy asked the question with his face the picture of worried enquiring innocence.

'They've gone out!'

'How much?'

'Thirty-four pounds. Makes me sick. I reckon them double that. Why didn't you tell us they were at the beginning of the sale? He was selling Lot 10 when we came in and then we had to get catalogues.'

'I don't know, Reg, if I'm not here to do the bidding for the lot of you, it always comes unstuck somewhere. Hang it all, you would think some-one would have bought them. I oughtn't to have stopped talking to you outside there, Tom. They wouldn't have gone out if I'd been here. Who bought them?'

'Don't know yet. Bobbie Trewen and Jarwell are trying to find out. What else is here, Willy? You have viewed. It's well-nigh impossible to see anything now with this crowd pushing around.'

'Only a few lots. The best is gone. Butler's tray, and a few odds and ends. Fine dessert service but nearly all cracked—not worth much now. Better let me do the buying, then we can sort it out afterwards.'

'Hallo, Hamish. Found out who bought them?'

'Yes! The blinking porter, and he wouldn't tell me who he bought them for—"On commission for a private party"—that's all I could get out of him. I offered him a fiver to make them over to me and tell his customer he had made a mistake—bid on the wrong lot and let them go —but he wouldn't play. Seems we have lost them. If we hadn't been messing about in those stables it wouldn't have happened. Found out where that sundial's gone yet? Old ones are worth money!'

The sale dragged on, and some half an hour later found all the trade together again outside on the gravel drive. The rain had stopped and the ground was steaming dry. It was sticky and hot and almost opening time.

'I'm not so certain I want to stay on here,' said Reg. 'Very disappoint-ing sale. One would think by the look of the house that there'd have been some decent stuff here. I'm off to view the other sales. What are we going

I

to do about the butler's tray and the service? Settle it amongst ourselves now, before it's bought?'

'Not a bad idea. What about——'

'Hey! Who's the poor mug to stay on here and do the buying?'

'Willy! He landed that job on himself half an hour ago,' cut in Tom before any other suggestions were made. 'He said if he didn't do all the buying everything went wrong.'

'So he did. Good oh! Shaun stays on here.'

Willy made a show of reluctance that was easily overcome.

'Let's get the lots settled. Who wants the dessert service?'

Everyone did. In the end they were all knocked out except Reg, who claimed it from Jarwell at forty-six pounds.

'Got that, Willy? Buy the service for me up to fifty pounds—that's what I reckon it. What about the butler's tray?'

'Everybody has that weighed up,' said Bobbie Trewen. 'A tenner is the long and short of that one.'

'Anybody reckon it more than that?'

'No, all there at that price—never can make any money out of butlers' trays.'

'All agreed?' enquired Willy. 'Then the ayes have it. The tray will be mine. I am going another ten shillings—got an order for as many as I can find. What about the coal-scuttles and paper-mâché trays?'

'You can have all of them as far as I'm concerned. The trays are too anaemic in design, and you can never buy a copper or brass coal-scuttle at a house sale—not with any profit left in it, anyway.'

'O.K., Reg. Anybody else want them?'

'I do,' said Peter Nebbing. 'I want the trays.'

'Start the bidding, then.'

'Two pounds.'

'Look, Peter, if you think I've got any hope of buying three papier-mâché trays in there against all that mob for two pounds, then you can forget it. Do you want them more than seven pounds ten?'

'No, but I'm in the settlement on them up to that price.'

'You are nothing of the sort. I'm not putting ten shillings in your pocket just from a philanthropic urge. You clear off and be content with what you may have on the service. I'll pass the money over to Tom, if there is any. Is it all finished? Oh, by the way, I'll try to find out what happened to the sundial while I am waiting. See you tonight, Tom, for the information on the other sales.'

As the others departed Willy said quietly: 'We'll settle the chandeliers then. I didn't see why all that crowd should have a picking out of them. Wouldn't have minded Reg, but the rest—*paugh*! Anyway, they should get up in the morning. What made you all so late getting here?'

'We went to the wrong village—met up with Jarwell there. I heard the sale was at Cuddlington. We stopped at the outskirts of the village and asked an old gaffer the way to the sale. Apparently, from what I could gather, he had just come out of a doctor's surgery or something. Blooming old fool—directed us round the back of beyond!'

After they'd all gone, Willy singled out the porter.

'Good man! Thirty-four for the pair, wasn't it?'

'Yes. That's right. Some of your friends wanted me to tell them who I had bought them for. One of them offered me a fiver to transfer them to him.'

'Yes, I heard all about it. I think you had better pay for them yourself, rather than have them transferred in my name. There's the money and a fiver for your trouble. You earned it.'

It was a large tip, but likely to pay dividends on some future occasion.

There was some stiff opposition on the dessert service. A friend of the family gave it a hard run. It was finally secured at a cost of forty-two pounds, which meant no knockout money for anyone except Jarwell, who would draw two pounds from Reg Bardon. The butler's tray cost eight pounds ten shillings—thirty shillings to divide amongst ten men—three shillings each. Would not even cover petrol money. The papier-mâché trays started at five pounds and finished up at nine pounds ten. Willy could not even get a bid in for them.

At last, after a long idle wait, the silver salt-shaker came up well hidden at the bottom of the box; he secured the lot for the sum of three pounds. Then he sought out the clerk, transferred the dessert service to Reg Barden —after some argument on the correctness of that procedure—paid his own bill and got permission to remove everything from the sale. Porters usually object to that happening while the sale is in progress but porters do not always collect six pounds on one commission. This one could not do enough for Willy, helping him pack and load into the car.

When the box of assortments came out, Willy began to unload it on the gravel drive—cups, saucers, butter-dishes, a tin-opener, a cheese-grater, a tea-pot lid, six jam-jars . . .

'I don't want all this rubbish. There's only one item any good to me.'

As the things came out one after another and he got down to the bottom of the box, his puzzled expression gave way to alarm, and then to anger. The silver Queen Anne salt-shaker was not there.

'Anything wrong, sir?'

'Yes, there is! I bought this heap of junk for the sake of one item— paid three pounds for it. Some thieving rat has gone and swiped it. I put it down underneath the other things at the bottom of the box and remember covering it over with this metal cheese-grater. That's still there but the other thing has gone.'

'What was it, sir? Anything any good?'

'Yes, it was. What it was doesn't matter.'

Willy saw the futility of making any enquiries or of going to the auctioneer to disclaim the purchase. If he demanded the return of his money because one thing was missing from a box full of oddments, awkward questions would be asked.

He threw all the oddments back into the box and loaded it into his vehicle. In one of the local Torminster sale-rooms that box of tricks, if sold in two separate lots, might bring back his three pounds again. He went home in something of a temper. Somebody at that sale knew a thing or two about silver and knew a thing or two about stealing. Nothing to look at, that little salt-shaker, but very rare—worth a profit of over fifty pounds, though it hardly weighed two ounces. Reg? Tom?—no. Bobbie? Dickie?—no. Jo or Peter?—not likely. Neither of them would hesitate to hide something if they got the chance, but steal—no. More likely to be that Jarwell fellow. Too much of the gentleman's manners about him. Quiet, shirky. He would be the one all right. It's certainly a trade nick. Not the kind of thing the ordinary sort of sale-room petty pilferer would know enough about to steal. Any private person know-ledgeable enough to have recognized its worth would have had a go at it under the hammer. Ten to one it is Jarwell.

That evening, after going home for tea, he motored over to Tom's shop. Tom had not been home very long, because his car was still out-side, and as Willy passed it the reek of hot oil given off by a cooling engine stung the back of his nostrils and throat. Time old Tom got him-self a new car, he thought. That one has just about had its day—smells as if it uses more oil than petrol.

'Come in,' said Tom, opening the private side door in response to Willy's knock. 'The wife's not here—staying with some relatives—only just got back a few minutes.'

Tom looked a bit uncomfortable when Willy's eyes ran round the room taking in all the untidiness and muddle.

'When the cat's away and all that, you know. What with being on the go all day long—doesn't leave much time for tidying up. I will cop it when she comes back, but there it is—can't do everything. Have something to eat?'

'No thanks, Tom. I've had mine, but you can pour me out a drink if you like.'

'Sure, and you may need it. I got home nearly an hour ago. There was a piece of paper stuffed in the door. Would I go round and see Mrs Prater as soon as I returned? Urgent. I've just come back from seeing her. She is all of a tizzwazz. Wow, boy! Is there a row going on about Bert Hammond's table! As far as I gather from the old lady, he took it up to London. One of his friends queried it being genuine. He takes it to three or four of the top-notch dealers and the table is turned down flat—absolute fake. One dealer intimated that he had seen the table before somewhere down in the West Country. This bloke bounces back on the auctioneer and demands the return of his money—threatened court action and all sorts of things. Old Hickory wasn't having any, however, and referred to the conditions of sale displayed on the front page of the catalogue. You know—no responsibility for misdescription, etc. He promised the chap to look into the matter, perhaps get more information from the past owner. He called on old Mrs Prater this morning. Nearly frightened the life out of her with all his formal language and talk of court cases. Poor old soul—she certainly earned that fiver! Stuck to her guns. She told me she said: "What's sold is sold. I put the table in the sale. It sold. I've been paid and that's that. How long it's been in my family is nobody else's business but me own. I came by it honestly and if you go and tell lies about it in your catalogue, that's nothing to do with me. I don't know any more about it than you do."

'It seems old Hickory went off not entirely satisfied. To tell you the truth, Willy, I'm a bit worried about the whole thing. I'm the one who will take the can back. Are we on the underside of the law?'

'Do you know if Mrs Prater had to sign a declaration as to ownership when she put the table in the sale?'

'No, she didn't. I asked her that myself.'

'We are all right then. Can't touch us. If the truth has got to come out in court then she acted as your agent, and you were acting for Bert Hammond through me. Court cases like that are very, very expensive—

what are known as "lawyers' delights"—nobody gets anything out of them except the legal profession, and they drawl them out as long as they can for obvious reasons. It won't come to a court case. The cheque went through all right. We have all had our money—forget it, Tom.'

'What about that bit of silver you mentioned? Did you get it?'

'I'm seeing red on that, Tom. It was a neat little salt-shaker. I stuff it down to the bottom of the box—buy the lot for three pounds, go to collect it—no salt-shaker. Somebody swiped it. Trader, too. Couldn't have been anybody else. You got any ideas, Tom?'

'Like that, was it? Not the first complaint I've heard when a certain party has been at a sale. No names no pack drill but he lives a long way away and his surname might begin with "J".'

'That's just who I have in mind. Ah, well! It's a long lane that has no turning. What about the other sales, Tom? The Chiddermesle one reads well from the catalogue.'

'Reads well but looks to me like a dealer's plant. Too many Pembroke tables—nine of them—all been done up a bit and one or two smelling of cabinet-maker's polish. What sort of house would possess nine Pembroke tables, I ask you?'

'Ropey?'

'I reckon so.'

'Getting rid of one of his rejected export orders?'

'We met him there while we were viewing. He was pricing them in his catalogue but I think that was only bluff.'

'That accounts why he wasn't over at Caddington. Not like him to miss a sale. Too busy watching trade reaction on his own goods. He is a silly man. If he wanted to unload Pembroke tables I could have done with three or four of them—so could you. Why on earth does he have to stick them in a sale?'

'Oh, Ropey is always after the last penny. You can bet your bottom dollar he will have some sticky reserves on them. By the way, if you want to put his back up and annoy him, tell him about the big deal you had with the American. Ropey was the only one he did not call on. No one gave him Ropey's address.'

'Can't wonder at that, Tom, either. He's so bally sarcastic. You never see him smile unless someone else has gone down the drain with a hot lot. Still, by and large he does well for himself—with that cousin of his over in America. If you ask me, Master Ropey has got a nice little packet of dollars tucked away in the free country. What could be easier? Take tea-caddies, for instance. They can be bought by the dozen over here for fifty shillings to three pounds each. Over there those same tea-caddies retail at anything between thirty and sixty dollars—ten to twenty pounds each. They wouldn't cost more than ten shillings each to get them there. Look at the profit! Butlers' trays fetch eighty pounds. Admittedly costs are higher, but if Ropey is invoicing his goods at a low figure, just enough to show a profit on his books, the greater the profit when they sell in America. He dodges heavy tax this end because his profit is small and pays very little tax the other end because taxation is nothing like so heavy. When he has got enough salted away he can cock a snook at a country whose business may very well be wrecked on the rocks of Administration and Socialism. Believe you me, Tom, Ropey is sitting pretty. I wish I had a relative I could trust out there.

'Well, I must be getting along. What about the chandeliers, by the way?'

'I don't feel I've any moral right to any knockout on them, Willy. After all, they were bought before any of us set eyes on them—you had everyone up the garden path. No one but me has the slightest idea you bought them. Are they up to me?'

'Of course they are—said so this morning. After all, you did me a good turn. With what I paid the porter, they cost forty pounds.'

'Shall we knock 'em out or give and take?'

'Oh, give and take. I bought them—you offer.'

'I'll either give or take a tenner, Willy.'

'Pay you out the tenner, Tom. You need not have let me down that lightly—business is business. I reckon them over seventy-five to sell. Here's two fivers. Thanks for the drink. Why don't you come out for supper one night?' Willy took in the disorder, the lack of comfort, as he turned to go. 'Ethel was only saying the other day it was quite a time since she'd seen you.'

Was Tom's wife a wrong 'un? Willy wondered. Surely not. She'd always seemed a quietish sort of woman. But all this staying with relatives . . . Tom, of course, would never say a word.

Willy had not very long to wait before, quite by chance, he was able to confirm his suspicions about who had boned the salt-shaker. He got home towards the end of a hot and particularly frustrating day to find that Isaac Demarcus, a big London silver dealer, had called, and was coming back.

'Oh—and a man from the National Insurance people came, dear!'

'I'm going to have a bath,' he told Ethel. 'If Demarcus comes back before I'm down, keep him talking in the showroom. As for that bum from the Ministry—oh God!' he groaned, 'it's ages since I put any stamps on! That's what he must be after. I shan't see him . . . you'll have to.'

'A *bath*?' she shouted after him. 'At *this* time?' But the bathroom door had already banged. She shrugged her shoulders, knowing better than to press the matter. When Willy was in that sort of mood . . .

In fact, Willy felt, he'd never needed a bath more. No need to alarm Ethel . . . never hear the end of it. He piled his clothes on a piece of newspaper, poured half a bottle of disinfectant into the water and soaked himself in it. He had just come from one of the filthiest cottages his questing spirit had ever taken him into, spurred on by a chance word about a chest of drawers from the landlord of the Black Dog, a pub in a remote moorland village. Together he and Albert Twistle—who had chalked up quite a score against the owner of the chest, and hoped to recoup himself through the proceeds of the sale—picked their way up the stairs of the cottage, Willy breathing only when he had to, and resolutely concentrating on the matter in hand. The chest was a good one— enough light through the cracked and cobwebbed panes to see that.

Cross-banded top—good feature. Walnut all right—oyster-shell— lot of it gone—can't see the rest for dirt. Drawer-fronts seem O.K.— no worm showing—original handles by the look of it—yes, must be original—nice set—one gone. Lot of the oyster veneer gone from the front too—veneer heaving and lifting off in places—must be the damp causing that. Bottom moulding there—bit gone off one side—original elongated bun feet—William and Mary—sides plain veneered, no oyster. H'm, unusual drawer linings. Made of oak with side runners, not bottom runners—usually find side runners in the Jacobean period—must be early William and Mary—can't see any worm in the drawer linings. Phew, don't these clothes inside whiff! Smells as if a rat had died in a drawer . . . better have a look at the back of it.

His mind was more or less made up. It had to be bought, provided the back was all right. The back was full of worm—take a lot of the profit out of it, having the thing restored. All the same, he'd take it—at a price. Between them they got it down into the sunshine.

Then: 'Hey!' he shouted, jumping back and automatically brushing his sleeves, the front of his clothes. 'Look at that!' As well as the worm-holes, the back was pocked with little black stains. And there was a reddish-brown thing moving—rather like a ladybird . . . and another . . . 'Bugs!'

The thing was alive with them. All the way home—and he'd made a quick getaway, leaving the landlord and his defaulting customer, an old woman, standing dejectedly on the path—he'd tended to squirm, conscious of an itch between the shoulder-blades.

To his relief the itching proved to be psychological. All the same, he'd have to get his clothes out of the house somehow and have a look later.

By the time he was changed, Ethel had Demarcus downstairs in the showroom.

'Hello, Mr D. How are you? Had a good trip?'

'Yes and no. I came down to do an important valuation and took the opportunity of touring round to see what I could buy. Have you anything for me? There doesn't seem to be anything in your showroom.'

Willy looked towards a small mahogany cupboard under the window. He couldn't afford to let Demarcus go away empty-handed. A couple of lots would have to come out of his private hoard. Pity, because Demarcus always paid by cheque and the stuff in there was a cash deposit. He brought out a good George III coffee-pot and a set of six silver spoons by Hester Bateman, the late-eighteenth-century lady silversmith.

Demarcus squinted down his nose to examine the hall-marks of both lots, examining the spoons in detail to see that all were matching for pattern, engraving and date. The coffee-pot came in for an even more thorough examination. Not a dent or a scratch was missed.

'What does it weigh?'

'Forty-two ounces.'

'And the spoons?'

'The weight of the spoons doesn't matter, neither does that of the coffee-pot, if it comes to that. Weight has got nothing to do with value, except in the case of scrap silver. If only you silver merchants wouldn't try to come the old one about "so much per ounce" you would do your buying quicker and in a better atmosphere.'

'How much do you want for the pot?'

'Seventy-two.'

'Too much. Could buy it cheaper than that in London.'

'Could you? I wonder! Hundred or more, up there, would be nearer the price. I go up to Town now and again, you know.'

Demarcus wrinkled his nose. Shaun's no fool, he said to himself.

The trouble with him is that he is never hard up and anxious to sell. 'Come on now, let's get down to earth. What is the best on it? I want to buy but at least I want to buy it at a price on which I can see a profit.'

'Sixty-seven ten and don't hang about on it. You'll waste your own time and mine as well. The pot's worth that and I know it. Perfectly plain, good-shaped lid, no embossing, a good maker, and hall-mark.'

'I know, I know, but it has its price. Is fifty-two ten any good?'

'Not a bit. Let's forget it and see about the spoons.'

'We'll come to them in a minute. I'll give fifty-five for the pot, and that is my very last price.'

'Sixty-five or it goes back in the cupboard.'

That figure really was Willy's last price. He knew it to be well worth that money. It had cost him fifty pounds three years previously.

'I'll think about it.'

Demarcus intended to buy it at sixty-five pounds. He sensed that was Shaun's lowest price. He himself was assured of fifteen pounds profit on it, probably more. It was a fine coffee-pot, better than average, but there was no point in saying yes till he knew what Shaun wanted for the spoons. The coffee-pot could be used as a lever to bring the price down on the spoons.

'Now what about those spoons?—poor quality, not her best, and one is badly marked. I suppose you want more than you have a hope of getting just because they are by Hester Bateman?'

Demarcus was right when he said the spoons were of poor quality. Nearly every piece of silver which bears the mark of 'HB' is of almost silver-paper thickness, but the design, carefully and daintily executed, is typical of the Adam period. By and large, he considered she was a very much over-rated silversmith, by no means the best or the earliest of the eighteenth-century women silversmiths. Willy knew all about the Hester Bateman Club in America however—a club formed by persons all intent on collecting her work. That in itself was sufficient to make prices soar.

'For the spoons? Oh, seventeen pounds ten.'

That's something he doesn't know the value of, thought Demarcus. Got him on these! Get thirty-five for them without batting an eyelid. 'Eighty for the two lots.'

Willy did not hesitate very long. He had walked in just as Tom was unloading a box of silver which had been acquired from a private address. Picking out the spoons, which Tom had not properly appraised, he bought them for five pounds the six, catching Tom well and truly on one foot.

'Fair enough. Can't make it cash, I suppose?'

Demarcus shook his head. 'Sorry, boy. I never carry cash on me. Cheques always keep the books straight too.' He gave Willy a sly look and upheld the reputation of the silver dealers as the best payers in the antique business by producing his cheque-book and writing out the cheque. None of this 'send me up an invoice and we will send the money on' business all too prevalent in other branches. To Willy a deal without money was like a bottle of wine gone sour.

'Bought very much this trip?'

'Not a great amount, but had a very nice buy in the way of a Queen Anne kitchen salt-shaker. Had to pay for it, but I'm very pleased to have it.'

A peculiar expression passed for a split second over Willy's face.

'Really, Mr Demarcus? Do you know, I have never seen one at close quarters before in my life. Would it be asking you too much to show it to me?'

'Not at all. I have it out in the car. If you like to come out, I will show it to you.'

After rummaging about in a large cardboard box he eventually produced the salt-shaker and handed it to Willy—who turned it over very carefully in his hand, closely examining the marks.

It was the same one—no doubt about it. Maker 'BA', same date and everything—couldn't be stretching coincidence so far for two of these to be around. Without doubt the one that was swiped from his box.

He made a shot in the dark.

'You bought this from Jarwell.'

Demarcus lifted one eyebrow and his eyes narrowed. His transaction had been private so he gave a shrug, making Willy certain of his ground.

'*You got this from Jarwell.* How much did you give him for it?'

'Sorry, my transaction was confidential.'

'The lousy, twisting, thieving blighter! Do you make a habit of buying stolen goods—confidential purchases of course?'

'What do you mean? I don't like that remark.'

'You answer my first question and I'll answer yours, sir.'

'As a matter of fact I did buy it from him. What do you know about it? I thought you said you'd never seen one before in your life? How do you know all about Jarwell having one?'

'I apologize, Mr Demarcus—that wasn't strictly true, but I had a hunch and wanted to see the one you bought. They are quite rare, and it was too much of a coincidence that you should purchase another one of that date in the district. By rights it belongs to me.'

When Willy had told his story, Demarcus grunted.

'Sure it's the same one?'

'Absolutely certain. I'm not likely to forget it.'

'I can't say that your way of trying to make sure of it was particularly nice, but it was honest enough. I think I'll stop the cheque I gave and send the wretched thing back to him. I don't like this sort of business.'

'No, don't do that. You bought it in good faith. How much did you give him?'

'Sixty-five pounds. Couldn't buy it for any less, but he can have it back.'

'As far as I'm concerned, the matter is over and done with. You bought it and have paid for it. It's yours, and good luck to you with it. I can settle my account with Jarwell my own way.'

Demarcus turned the cylindrical-shaped piece of silver over in his hand. One didn't buy them every month of the year and he had been very pleased to acquire it from Jarwell, but he didn't like buying stolen goods, even though the legitimate owner had waived all claim to it. Shaun was obviously a good loser.

'You can tell Jarwell the next time you see him that I have bought the last lot I will ever buy from him.' He meant it.

Willy shook his head.

'No, I will never tell him. He will never know that I know. There are more ways than one of killing a cat.'

For the sake of sixty-five pounds Jarwell had lost a good customer and made a formidable enemy.

Demarcus departed, not so happy with his little prize. A hard buyer, he had a higher standard of honesty and straight dealing than some of his colleagues.

Half an hour after Demarcus's departure, Willy was strolling round his little property; his day was ending better than it had begun. For one thing, he'd got his clothes out of the house and into an out-house and the closest inspection hadn't revealed a single trace of bugs. Then there was the business about Jarwell . . . *very* satisfactory. (He hadn't long to wait for his revenge. Three months later he saw to it that Jarwell, who knew nothing about pictures, paid one hundred and fifty pounds for

one worth about twenty pounds. He also arranged that the picture should
be damaged beyond repair before ever it left the sale-room. 'An eye for
an eye . . .' is the harsh law of the dealers' world.)

Ethel came out and they walked down the vegetable garden, within
sound of the new tennis court.

'Who's Ann got out there today? They seem a better crowd—anything rather than that Art School riff-raff.' Willy despised modern
painting almost as much as he did Income Tax inspectors—and for more
or less the same reason to him—they were both a ruddy public swindle,
earning good money for doing sweet Fanny Adams.

'The two Coxes. And one of the Seager girls.'

'Flying high, aren't we?' He pinched Ethel in a forbidden zone.

'Stop it, Willy! And what do you mean, "flying high"?'

'Those Seager girls—father the County sheriff, big landowner and
goodness knows what, with a wife who looks through me when we meet.'

'Ann's been over there twice—she and the Seagers are good friends,
the girls say our court's much better than theirs. As for Mrs S., you've
only yourself to blame.'

Willy's straight look and plain speaking weren't to everyone's liking
—if he thought anyone was 'toffee-nosed' he took no trouble to hide it.

'Hmph! And that Cox boy—getting too fond of Ann, too free with
her altogether. Farmers' sons live too near to nature for my liking. They
get ideas.'

'Ann's growing up, dear,' Ethel replied, as she so often did. Since
leaving school and working as a secretary for the best solicitors in
Torminster Ann had changed. 'She's a young lady now. She can look
after herself.'

They could see the court now. The game had stopped and the four
were lounging back in deck-chairs outside the summer-house. A nice
summer-house, too—cost him twenty-five pounds at a sale and eighteen
to get it home and reassembled. When Ann raised her brown arm and
waved, Willy and Ethel, arm in arm, gave each other a little squeeze as
they turned away.

Yes, life was good. So good that Willy, hearing the sound of a car
in the drive, couldn't work up his usual indignation. It was the man from
the National Insurance, of course, and as it turned out he didn't want to
see Willy about his own stamps at all. It was Willy's jobbing gardener
he was on the ferret about. Willy's conscience was clear: part of the
gardener's wages were put down as expenses—if he, Willy, wanted his

premises looking prosperous and tidy to impress customers that was a legitimate business expense.

'No doubt. But it's his card I want to see. He works for you on the Monday so you are the employer responsible for stamping his card.'

'*His card?*' Willy said hoarsely. 'He's never had a card!'

They went into the matter in tedious detail.

'You realize you're liable for prosecution in a case like this—don't worry,' the inspector went on hastily, 'we seldom resort to prosecution provided the defaulter accepts his proper responsibility.'

'Well, I'm damned!' Willy brought his fist down on the table. 'If it isn't one thing it's another!'

'I quite sympathize with you, Mr Shaun. I know how you must be feeling, but I have my job to do. Render unto Caesar the things . . . and all that.'

'I could give *you* a quotation but it wouldn't help. One thing's certain: Elkins can't pay his part of the back money, I know that. I wouldn't ask him for it. If you'll tell me the extent of the damage I'll settle up right away.'

'I'm afraid it can't be done quite that way. It's not within my scope to inform you how much you owe—not my department, you see. You'll have to go to your local National Insurance Office, get the necessary forms . . .'

Willy sat down.

'These payments, now. They'll be liable to an income tax rebate, won't they?

'Again, sir, that's not my department. Perhaps a visit to your local tax officer——'

'Have a drink!' Willy was so flabbergasted that he could think of nothing else to say.

And the blighter accepted, he thought later, as he was sitting down to his first square meal of the day. It was human after all—and *me* pouring out a drink for a damn snooper in my own house! After he's just caned me for pounds and pounds. . . . I must be getting old. Losing my grip.

11 *The Bachelor's Chest*

It was, in fact, one of those weeks. The following day, at a large private sale, his 'knockout' friends dropped a very hot item on to him—to the tune of four hundred and seventy-five pounds. It was the only piece of antique furniture to arouse real interest, apart from a pair of painted Sheraton period armchairs which he also held, for forty-eight pounds, in the settlement after the sale. He was not worried about these. They would show a small profit, but he was worried about his bachelor's chest of drawers. Apart from the price it was a gem, and no mistake. Two feet five inches wide, pull-out slides, fall-over top, walnut veneers and herringbone inlay, a glorious colour, handles original with fine patina around them—the piece could not be faulted. There were three London men present at the settlement and Willy, knowing that by hook or by crook a day's work somehow had to be got out of the chest, reckoned these three would not be content with less than eighteen to twenty pounds each, even if it meant one or other of the three holding a hot lot. As the bidding went round and round three or four faded out quite quickly. As each man ducked the bidding a different calculation had to be made because the amount per person increased as the number left in the bidding diminished. Willy's reckoning had been at fault. As it became more and more of a gamble who was going to have a sizzling hot lot dropped on him, the London crowd, by instinct, decided that sixteen pounds ten would constitute a day's work.

Willy had been left holding the baby.

'Serve him right. Time he had a banger. He can afford to hold a hot lot with a car like he has got. Can hold a few more in the future too as far as I'm concerned. We are all right—got a day's work out of it. Reckon he'll lose a hundred and fifty on that one.'

Yes, Willy knew what remarks were being made and also was aware that every dealer of consequence would soon know that he had been 'dropped' with a batchelor's chest of drawers which cost too much money.

What about Bruno Hammers? Taking the garage proprietor at his word he had unloaded one or two things on to him, but these had all been in the hundred-pound region. It was by no means certain that B.H. would rise to a five-hundred-pounder, with not much to see for the money.

The first thing he had taken over to him had been a large mid-eighteenth-century silver salver—a real showy lot. He had managed to get it from a dealer who didn't appreciate its real value for forty-five pounds—roughly one pound per ounce. The current market value of the salver was anything between ninety and a hundred pounds. He had sold it to Hammers for fifty-five pounds, giving him a long sales talk about quality, design, investment, and so on. Everything went over Bruno's head except the investment side of the transaction. He bought it, paid for it in five-pound notes, and, as soon as Willy had departed, wrapped the salver up in brown paper, tucked it under his arm and went straight along to a good silver dealer with whom he had a nodding acquaintance.

'Do me a favour, will you? The wife's had this given to her by an old aunt who is disposing of her belongings before the Government can get their fingers on any of it by way of death-duties. It is supposed to be quite valuable. What value can I put down for insurance purposes?'

'Let's have a look at it. Yes—a good salver, right design for the period, which is important. Let's see—weight forty-five ounces six pennyweights. Date 1763—London made. Yes, let's see—I think we ought to value it at one hundred and twenty pounds for insurance purposes. That figure is slightly in excess of its market value.'

'Supposing my wife decided to sell it, what would you be prepared to give for it?'

'That's a different matter, sir. We do not make offers; you would have to tell us how much you wanted.'

'Queer chaps, you are. What are you frightened about? We have to make offers all day long in the motor trade.'

'Yes, I know you do, but you have a little book, published every month, which tells you what to offer for every make of second-hand car, taking into account all such details as mileage and condition. All you have to do is to look it up. We don't have anything like that to guide us. Ours is all brainwork and personal experience of current market values. We don't give that knowledge away very readily. We used to, but people with things to sell have got so artful we no longer make offers. Do you blame us?'

'No, I don't suppose I do, but if I was to say to you, "I want seventy-five pounds for this salver," would you buy it?'

'Yes, sir, we would, and possibly be prepared to give a little more. We would like to be given a chance to buy it should your wife decide to part with it. Will you let us know?'

'Yes, I will. How much do I owe you for the valuation?'

'Three guineas, please. That is our minimum valuation charge.'

This shook Bruno Hammers. He was quite expecting him to say: 'That's quite all right, sir. Pleasure to do it for you.' He paid without a murmur and returned home very satisfied with his purchase. He had not believed Shaun when the latter had said the salver was worth seventy pounds or more and would appreciate steadily in value. He had his proof now. Decent sort of chap, Shaun. Obviously could be relied on.

This transaction started Bruno's interest in antiques. He could see money in the game; not that he wanted to sell anything he might buy. The whole idea was to get rid of the huge stacks of five-pound notes he had acquired—get rid of them discreetly and safely. Still, it was satisfying to know that he could already get a profit on what he had bought.

K

After that, he'd taken anything Willy brought over without a murmur. But five hundred pounds? Willy wondered. It was a lot of money. He's got it—got loads of it, but I don't know—he may not be game enough for that amount. I'll try him, anyway. Got to get rid of it somehow. He could still feel the hot sickly wave which had swept over him when he realized that the others had landed it on to him. He had succeeded in appearing to make light of it, but he was unlikely to forget the sight of his money being counted out and disappearing into other men's pockets —money some of which was unlikely to be recovered. It was then that he had realized what Peter Nebbing's feelings must have been when the pottery font was 'dropped' on him.

He picked up the telephone and asked for the Tormouth number. ... 'Hallo. Is that you, B.H.? Shaun of Torminster here. Yes, fine, thank you—and you? Have you? Well, if you couldn't who else could? No, not really. The main reason was that I have just acquired a very fine piece of furniture. I've been selling you quality rather than quantity so thought you might like a chance to buy it. No, it is a bachelor's chest of drawers. Yes, I said bachelor's chest. No, old man, the fact that you are married is no reason at all why you would not be wanting to buy it. It is just a name given to a very rare type of Queen Anne period small chest of drawers. It is in walnut—very small. Five hundred and fifty. Yes, I said five hundred and fifty. Well, it's difficult to describe it properly on the phone. You will have to see it. Not very well, that's the trouble. I have a London dealer coming down to see another bit I have. Coming tomorrow morning. He'll want to buy this bachelor's chest as soon as he sees it. I would rather sell it to you ... well, you pay up on the spot—he doesn't—takes several weeks to get the money out of him. ... No, I couldn't do it in the time. What about you making a trip over this evening? ... Do a crawl round the village pubs, if you like. I know of one where he makes his own potato whisky—burns your stomach lining out if you drink too much of it. You will? Seven o'clock will be fine with me. You can have dinner with us. Why not bring your wife? ... No? All right, see you later. Goodbye, B.H.'

Whew, he breathed to himself, he's biting! He's biting!

He spent the rest of the afternoon rearranging the furniture in the front room to show off the walnut bachelor's chest in proper surroundings. It looked far better than it had done in the sale-rooms. Having hooked his fish all that now remained was to land it.

Bruno Hammers arrived in the evening, was conducted into the front room and shown the chest of drawers. He let out a long, low whistle.

'What! Five hundred and fifty pounds for that?'

Willy carefully explained all the points—the age, the genuineness, the rarity, the desirability—in fact, everything. He played on the quality theme, impressing on B.H. the fact that quality coupled with rarity and the two combined in a small piece of furniture for which there was an ever increasing demand meant a very steep price. He told B.H. point blank that he did not mind at all if he decided not to buy it, as he could sell it when and where he chose. That finished B.H. Knowing nothing about it, he wanted it. A haggle started over the price which Willy cut short by refusing to budge from the quoted price of five hundred and fifty pounds—cash. Now certain of his fish, he adopted an attitude of having done B.H. a favour by letting him have this prize item.

'Haven't got anything like that amount of cash on me. Will you trust me?'

'You know better than to ask. Tell you what we'll do. I've got to come over to a sale at Tormouth tomorrow—I'll bring the chest with me. It will be safer in my brake than in the back of your car. It is a five-hundred-and-fifty-pounder and you can't afford to take any chances with it—rare lot you know, B.H.!'

The buying and selling done, they paid visits to four local pubs. B.H. was disgusted with the 'skirts behind the bars', as he put it. 'Wouldn't do for Tormouth, boy. With legs like that one's got, lose more customers than keep them.'

Willy could not understand B.H. when it came to this sort of thing. He had a charming wife—quiet and soft-spoken, good-looking too, yet every woman who had a flashy painted face, a good figure, and a shapely pair of legs, B.H. was after her like a shot out of a gun.

Next afternoon in the sale-room at Tormouth Tom found Willy in high spirits.

'Sold my chest, that's why,' was the reply he got in answer to his question.

'Not the bachelor's chest!'

'Sure thing—going to deliver it later today.'

'I bet you lost a packet on it and right down glad to get rid of it. I know I would be. You were a bit of a mug to stick your nose so far into that one. It was obvious that the London crowd didn't want it any more than any of us did—at that sort of price. It had to be dumped on someone and not them if they could help it.'

'The trouble with you, Tom, is that you can't reckon a good lot. You get cold feet. For your information, I held that chest deliberately and I—— Hallo, Reg.'

'He's sold his chest,' said Tom.

'Bet you lost a packet on it!'

'That's where you're wrong, Reg—both of you. I was saying to Tom when you arrived that just because a chap has got a bit more knowledge and can weigh up the value better than the others, it's not necessarily "dropped" on him. The others like to think so, but sometimes that is only wishful thinking. I sold it and earned myself a profit of seventy-five pounds, which is more than any of you got out of it.'

'Well I'm blessed. There is always a bigger mug than yourself somewhere, that's proved over and over again.'

'Think he's sold it, Reg, or just trying to keep his end up on it?'

'He's sold it all right, Tom. I know him—wouldn't be so cocky if he hadn't. Trade couldn't have bought it from him—too much money. He gets the luck of the devil. Me? I would have been forced into losing over a hundred had I been caught with it.'

The only two lots of any interest here—in the smallest and stuffiest of the four sale-rooms in Tormouth—had been bought by Bert Hammond for the ring. One or two of the local dealers were not members of the fraternity, but instead of opposing the ring at the auction sales they wisely refrained from attending, leaving things to sort themselves out, and then perhaps being able to get hold of anything they might be interested in from the dealer who 'held' it in the settlement.

Private opposition was negligible. Quite a number of people who would not hesitate to attend and bid their heads off at a sale in the biggest and principal sale-room in the town fastidiously avoided any sale in these particular rooms.

The first lot of interest was a mahogany Sheraton period breakfast table—a good one, with a delicate centre-pillar of fine proportions, a lovely faded crossbanded top, and a perfect set of castors on the four reeded splayed legs. The next was a real gambling lot—a bronze statue of Hercules, signed by 'Clodion'. The former cost twenty-eight pounds and the latter had been purchased for the maiden bid of fifty bob. The settlement was in the usual place—the private bar of the Red Lion, a public house next to the sale-room. There were eleven dealers present and four 'hooks and eyes'. These four, after a slight argument, were pushed off with one pound apiece before the ring formed up.

Willy had made up his mind about the table. He was going to hold it if he could. Limit sixty-five pounds. The bronze? Just don't know, he debated with himself. Could be right—not too happy about the colour. Should be the colour of dried pigeon's blood, but that doesn't help me —I've never seen dried pigeon's blood. Chances are it's a wrong 'un. Good copy probably. Weighs about one and a half hundredweight, I should think—worth nine quid to melt for scrap price. Think I'll risk twenty-five on it unless the bidding is exceptionally strong. Worth a lot of money if it is right though. Wonder what the others reckon it? Hell, I must get some knowledge of bronzes from somewhere.

Bert, as the local dealer in the biggest way of business, was acting as chairman, clerk, and treasurer all rolled into one.

Willy had some uneasy moments over the bronze, but kept on bidding nearly to the end and made three pounds fourteen shillings in the knock-out. It was bought by a local syndicate at a total cost of forty-seven pounds ten, and after their departure Ropey Stringer, rather surprisingly, was seen to be all smiles.

'They've got *that* one round their necks! It's no good—a wrong 'un, vetted by the local Museum two years ago—a copy.'

'How do you know so much about it?'

'Ssh! Happened to be mine. Wait!—I didn't put it in here. Sold it nearly two years ago for a tenner to a bloke who probably found out as much as I did—N.B.G. I scratched my private symbol on it before I sent it to the Museum, so I know it's the same one.'

'You had a bit of a nerve to stick in the bidding as long as you did.'

'Had to. Didn't want to fade on Bert, otherwise he would have been landed. One stops and the lot stops. The others thought I knew something about the bronze—I did, of course, but not what they thought.'

While they were all talking about the bronze, Willy had a quiet word with Bert Hammond about the Sheraton period breakfast table, which had been left with Bert at fifty-four pounds.

'I want the table,' said Willy. 'I haven't finished with it yet. Just between you and me now, we'll square it up later.'

When the others had gone he and Bert seated themselves comfortably at the window with a pint each.

'Now for the table, Bert. How does it stand? I mean, how much is it costing now?'

The door opened quickly and in came Ropey, Ticker, and Peter Nebbing.

'You chaps clear off,' said Willy. 'There is no more to come on the table. You all left it at fifty-four pounds.'

'Haven't come to settle the table. You can do that with Bert in a minute. All right, Bert. What about it?' There was a speculative sneer on Ropey's face as he addressed Bert.

'What about what?' Bert shifted slightly in the chair, a glint of suspicion in his eyes.

'Lot 226—various Staffordshire figures, etc. Saw you buy it with my own eyes. You bid from the wall but we were watching you. Checked up with the clerk afterwards, too—just to make certain. You bought that lot and it was down in your name on the book.'

'Yes. I did buy it, as a matter of fact. I saw no reason to put it up in the settlement. Who the devil wants three miserable Staffordshire figures? I sell that sort of Victorian rubbish to the tourists who come into the shop, but I can't think why they interest you—not trade goods at all.'

'It's not those figures we want. It's what was with them. Come off it, Bert. There was an early-Whieldon Staffordshire figure among them. You were one of the first to visit the sale. You got the porter to hide that figure in a cupboard and not to show it on the tray with the others when they were all held up for inspection just before the bidding started. I know all about it. You gave the porter ten shillings. The other one had his nose put out of joint; you should have given them five shillings each. That little bit of information was worth five bob to me. Ought to be ashamed of yourself! Where's the figure now?'

'Got it in my pocket.'

Bert sheepishly produced it. This was all news to Willy. He had not seen the Whieldon figure or even guessed of its existence.

'Well I'm blessed. Let's have a look at it. You twisting blighter, Bert Hammond.'

'Thought I'd got away with it. You got your stinking nose pushed into every blooming thing, Ropey.'

Willy examined the figure carefully. Period—bit on the crude side—early one, but the glazes are good—blue and green—yes, colours are right. Worth fifteen nicker if nothing. 'What did it cost you, Bert?'

'Two quid under the hammer,' answered Ropey for him. 'He can have the other three Staffordshire figures for the ten bob he gave the porter. He seems to want them for his tourist trade. Let's hope they help bring up the tone of his other goods.'

Ropey raised a laugh. The quality of some of Bert's stuff was questionable.

'At least I own a shop, all my own property and no mortgage. Some of us who have been in the trade for generations have forgotten more than others will ever know, especially when they haven't served inside a pr——'

'What's the time?' cut in Willy. The situation was getting ugly. Bert had a temper and Ropey never seemed to realize when others had had enough of his sarcasm. Ropey's last remark had stung Bert, who immediately hit back below the belt. It was well known that Ropey had been to prison—fourteen weeks for being involved in an accident while driving under the influence of alcohol—but no one ever referred to it.

'Five past six,' said Peter, producing a silver pocket watch the size of a cricket ball. 'I could do with a drink.'

A mean silence followed his statement. Everyone had the situation weighed up: five people—a small amount of business to transact—wouldn't last five rounds of drinks. The first one or two would pay for five, and the remainder would skedaddle off without standing their turn.

Ropey broke the awkward silence.

'So could I,' he said brightly. 'It's on you, Bert. You saved yourself a few bob when you paid out on the breakfast table. You can pay out of that.'

Bert got up and went out, returning within a minute.

'I've ordered beer, and,' looking at Ropey, 'if anyone wants "shorts" they can b-well go and buy them themselves. Let's get it over. Cost two quid.'

The bidding was stout, no one letting go until the Whieldon Staffordshire figure reached twenty pounds, and was left with Ropey.

'Pay out, Ropey. Eighteen on between five of us—that's three pound twelve apiece.'

('Eighteen on' referring to the fact that Bert had bought the figure for two pounds under the hammer.)

'What about the table now, Bert? I'll give or take six pounds on it.'

'I'll pay you out, Willy. I reckon it's worth more money—can always do with that sort of table in the shop—good sellers. There you are, one five and an odd. Oh! Just before you go, gentlemen, two shillings each, please.'

'What for?' was the chorus.

'Hire of this room. Cost ten shillings.'

'Why didn't you ask for a bob apiece when all eleven of us were here?' asked Ropey crossly.

'Because it would have broken your heart for me to make a shilling out of it. You would have wanted your penny change and I don't have anything to do with "coppers". Come on, stump up.'

They all paid up and left the room, all except one well pleased with their nine pounds odd from an easy quiet knockout.

On the way out Bert tapped Willy on the shoulder. 'One more for the road—on me. May as well spend this eight bob, not counting the two shillings which I am supposed to contribute. The landlord knows me well and there was no charge for the room. Just thought I would sting you all for the drinks I bought. Want a few sandwiches?'

'Perhaps I'd better,' said Willy, thinking of the evening's hard drinking ahead of him with Bruno Hammers.

When they'd carried the chest in and placed it in position in the Hammers' lounge, Bruno invited Willy into his library-cum-private-office, unlocked a cupboard which appeared to contain nothing but large cardboard boxes, took one box out, placed it on his green leather-covered flat-top desk, took the lid off the box, and exposed the contents to view. A sight for sore eyes. The box was full of five-pound notes.

'If I had that lot in there I would be scared stiff of burglars. Bit silly, isn't it?'

Bruno shook his head. 'The house is never left empty. Someone is always here, and anyway, if one did get in he would get more than he bargained for. Not every box contains money! I know which boxes to open and which to leave alone.'

Slowly the money was doled out, Bruno counting aloud, Willy silently until he interrupted the monotonous chant.

'Sorry, B.H. I'm not having that one.'

He picked it off the growing pile and laid it on one side.

'What's wrong with it?'

'Ten-pound notes are no longer legal tender—that's what is wrong with it.'

'Ten-pound note? So it is! How did that get in there, I wonder? Where were we? Better go back to the beginning, I've lost count.'

The five hundred and fifty pounds having been counted out and pocketed, the two set out for the usual. Out in the fresh air again, after closing time, Willy realized how muzzy his head was. He couldn't keep up with B.H. As it was, he had managed to pass some of his whiskies to other people, who received them quite happily, except one old vixen sitting at a nearby table, into whose glass Willy, unobserved, managed to pour three-quarters of a double whisky-and-soda. One sip was enough —old sour-face spat it out and created no end: she'd been drinking ginger ale.

On the way home he tried to calculate how much the evening had cost him. He could not think very clearly, so gave it up and concentrated hard on his driving. Home in the small hours, thankful to have made it, he got out of the car and locked it. The open air played havoc with him, he staggered, and the ground came up from somewhere and hit him. Slowly he got up on all fours and was violently sick. He was not used to drinking for the sake of drinking. He dragged himself to the back door, but could never afterwards remember having done so. Slumping himself into the easy chair in the kitchen he managed to get his shoes off.

Ethel went downstairs at 4 a.m. to make herself a cup of tea. She had been dozing fitfully, worried because her husband had not yet returned. Knowing where he had gone, and who he'd been with, she was anxious lest Willy had met with an accident.

What she saw when she switched on the kitchen light made her jump violently.

'Oh! So there you are.'

No answer. How could she expect an answer from a man who had gallantly fought a losing battle with something like fourteen double whiskies and was now sleeping it off, legs askew, arms dangling, and head lolling forward—out to the wide?

But he had sold his bachelor's chest!

12   *The Rockingham Cottages*

'Hallo there!'

Reg Bardon greeted Willy as the latter came in through his shop-door.

It wasn't very often that Willy paid a visit to Reg, whose shop was in the main shopping centre and whose prices were high. Reg catered for a good private clientele and seldom sold much to other local dealers; it would have been bad policy to let anything he had bought privately be seen on view in another local dealer's shop, the inference regarding who paid the best prices being obvious. But now and again he had a deal with Willy, who was different from the others, his stock not being on view to the public.

Passing the shop in his car Willy had spotted a small collection of Rockingham cottages displayed on a table in the window. Shaped like houses, churches, cottages, and castles, some with lift-off lids, all with proper chimneys and a hole in the back, these small, decorative, and much-sought-after pieces of porcelain were originally made to burn a pastille in, to overpower the unpleasant smells that often pervaded the dining-rooms of Georgian times. Occasionally one comes across a small cupboard in a sideboard, usually to one side of it, which may still retain the original receptacle provided for the gentlefolk of those days who were loth to 'leave the room'. These cottages are not rare, for thousands of them were made and there are still enough of them left to cause collectors no searching heartache. As they are not unduly expensive, they seldom remain in any dealer's shop for very long, being what the trade would refer to as a 'good selling line'.

Willy had inspected the collection in the window very carefully.

'Good morning, Reg,' was his answer. 'Nice little collection of cottages there in the window. How many have you got?'

'Ten. I only bought them yesterday—put them straight in the window —always sell—might even bring someone else in wanting to sell theirs—didn't even clean them up properly—some could do with a wash.'

'How much are you asking for them?'

'To you, Willy?—sixty pounds. I bought them reasonably enough and can pass them on the same, provided you don't sell them to be sold again in the town.'

By and large not a bad price—six pounds each. They were all brightly coloured, nicely fussy, which is what the ladies like, and although very dirty in the crevices, they were all in reasonably perfect condition.

'H'mph! Can I see a couple of them?'

'Sure you can. I'll get them all out.'

'Don't bother, Reg. Two will do—thanks. Thought so—yes. Look, Reg, it's none of my business—I'm not buying these—but I can tell you who you bought them from—a man with a shabby brown suitcase— a man whose aunt has just died and who left him a small collection of cottages which he didn't want—couldn't be bothered with them. Didn't know very much but knew they were valuable. Wanted to get rid of them altogether in one lot—didn't want to sell separately. All he wanted was three pounds apiece right through for the ten—thirty pounds in all. He knew that was reasonable enough for price but wanted to get rid of them. His wife didn't like old-fashioned knick-knacks, and he could do with a spot of cash.'

Reg looked at Willy and curled his tongue behind his teeth. Shaun was repeating word for word what the man had said who had sold him the Rockingham cottages not twenty-four hours previously—repeating it just as if he had been a hidden witness.

'You psychic or something? How do you know all about it? Did he offer them to you?'

'He did, Reg.'

'D'you mean to say you didn't buy them? Turned them down at three pounds apiece?'

'I did buy them.'

'You *bought* them? Then what am I doing with them? Bloke do the dirty on you and bring them to me to get a couple of pounds or so more?'

'He must have done the dirty on me in a way. I bought them all right. Ten of the nicest little Rockingham cottages I've seen for some time. The trouble is right now those ten are sitting in a china-cabinet in my show-room. Get me? I bought the blooming things last night—looked at them hard enough too. Couldn't see anything wrong with them and they were cheap enough. He came about six o'clock. The wife told him to come back because I was out. He said one of his relatives in the village had recommended him to see Mr Shaun. Had a car—an old black Ford. He seemed on the level, and I'm usually a good judge of my fellow men. Told me the story of his aunt dying and all that. The cottages wanted a good wash but I jumped at them for three pounds each—certain to double my money. He wanted cash—wouldn't take a cheque—said he didn't have a banking account and wanted the money right away—bit hard up—so cash it was. How did you pay, Reg? Cash or cheque?'

'Cash, I'm afraid. He told me he wanted the cash for the same reason. I normally insist on paying by cheque, but well, I ask you—ten Rockingham cottages, all perfect, for thirty quid?—I paid him in cash, but hang it all, old man, they can't be duds.'

'What are they, then? Stolen? Not on your life—somebody somewhere is making them. I'll bet a pound to a penny he's dropping them all over the countryside. That old black Ford will have been crammed full with them.'

'I wonder if the Trewens bought any, or old Sniffy up the road? Let's go up and see.'

There was no need to go in to ask. Occupying a prominent position in Sniffy's window were ten Rockingham cottages.

'I'll go in and have a word with him. Don't want him to make a fool of himself—he's a decent old stick. I can remember him in that shop when I was a boy. He was good to me—he and old Benson helped me over a good many stiles.'

'What the devil are we going to do about these cottages?' Reg said as Willy turned to go in. 'The whole place is flooded with them. I can't sell them in my shop—don't want that sort of thing. Genuine—yes, but I don't mess about with fakes or copies.'

'I'll give you a pound apiece for them to take them off your hands.'

Reg hesitated. 'No,' he said, 'I'll get rid of them somehow.' If they were worth a pound each to Shaun they were worth that and more to him. He was not prepared to lose twenty pounds quite so quickly.

Willy came out of Sniffy's shop with a grin on his face.

'Same again, Reg—another sucker! I told him he was old enough to be ashamed of himself. He's in there shedding tears as hard as diamonds. I took the liberty of using his telephone. Both the Trewens fell hook, line, and sinker. That glib-tongued bounder certainly worked hard in this area yesterday. Sure you won't take my offer for them, Reg?'

Cottages good enough to take him in, Reg Bardon, the two Trewens and, above all, old Sniffy, well then, they were good enough to pack off to the other side of the water. If the trade over here could hardly tell the difference then they certainly wouldn't be able to over there. He would send them off straight away to his contact in Toronto. Canada would be better than New York. News travels fast and it wouldn't be long before New York heard all about the fakes.

Going back into Reg's shop they took the cottages out of the window. A very close examination revealed certain give-away signs. The colours, particularly the green of the foliage, were too vivid. The gold line which appeared round the bases of a few was garish, not soft and covered with minute scratches and abrasions like the gilding on an old specimen. Some of the cottages had been deliberately overbaked in the firing kiln to give them a brownish appearance with a dirty crackled glaze—a good simulation of age. One thing in common with every one was the dust, inside and out. Thick dust looking as though it had been accumulating for years.

'I know what they did with them,' said Willy. 'Washed them in soapy water without rinsing them, and when they were nearly dry stuffed 'em in the bag of a Hoover and started the motor. When they were brought out again and thoroughly dry some of the grime was wiped away, leaving it well embedded in the crevices.'

'Well,' Reg dusted his knees and got up, 'we ought to be able to take a rise out of one or two of the boys in the sale-room. Coming?'

Being a view-day, the clan were gathering in one of the local sale-rooms. Although the upstairs floor of this tin-roofed building was crammed with stuff—chests of drawers three deep on top of each other, chairs, carpets, a couple of prams hanging from the rafters under the corrugated-iron sheeting, wardrobes, pictures, sideboard monstrosities, tables loaded to groaning point with bric-à-brac—there was not a decent antique in the sale.

A careful scrutiny of the catalogue had raised no hopes or interest but the sale had to be viewed all the same. Many a good lot had been discovered amongst rubbish such as this, casually or incorrectly described in the catalogue.

Reg, Willy, and Dickie Trewen were holding an animated conversation as Tom came plodding up the stairs.

' 'Morning, Tom,' was the general chorus.

'Phew! I'm not getting any younger. About time they held these sales downstairs. 'Morning all! How's the game? Anything here?'

'Nothing at all.'

Tom looked suspicious. That phrase 'nothing at all' had an old familiar sound. Seeing the look on his face, Willy said: 'Honest, Tom— not a sausage! By the way, how much do you want for your Rockingham cottages?'

There was some weak laughter from the other two at this question.

'How on earth did you know I had any? They are not for sale. I'm keeping them for a private customer of mine, she's coming in to see them this afternoon. This trade's haunted. I buy a few cottages from a private bloke, haven't breathed a word about them to a soul, and yet the whole world knows I've got them. Now how on earth can you account for it?'

'We just guessed it, that's all.'

Again there was a general laugh and Tom got nettled. He was having a rise taken out of him for some reason or other. How they knew he had those cottages was a mystery to him.

'Want to buy ten more, Tom?'

'Make it twenty, Willy. He can have mine as well.'

'You lot are jealous, that's what it is. Just because I happen to buy——'

'Tell him, somebody,' said Dickie, 'for Pete's sake tell him.'

'Tell me what?'

Tom was told, and his reply was rich in invective.

The sale-room was becoming crowded with people, poking here, prying there, catalogues in hand.

'Hear that, Willy?'

Tom almost spat it out between his teeth. Both had overheard a scathing remark passed by a loud-voiced woman to her friend as they poked about among the bric-à-brac. The words 'dealers . . . sale-room scum' could plainly be heard.

'You would think they were all mothers' innocents and only a dealer could work a dirty trick. Remember those wing-chairs?'

One lady customer had pasted a classic on to Tom which he had not forgotten. It was just after the war, when there was a scramble for goods of every description. The modern furniture manufacturers were not yet producing much, hampered as they were by quotas and restrictions, so there was a seemingly unending demand for second-hand furniture of all descriptions.

One morning a lady came into Tom's shop. She came straight to the point.

'I want a pair of walnut wing-armchairs.'

Tom pursed his lips. A mental vision of cabriole legs, shell-carved on the knuckle, original tapestry, flitted across his mind.

'Sorry, madam. I haven't anything like that in stock at the moment. A pair of genuine William and Mary or Queen Anne wing-chairs of that description would be a very rare item. Very expensive too.'

'Oh no. I don't mean old ones. Goodness me, I know what they would cost—perhaps a hundred and fifty pounds?'

'A lot more than that, madam, depending on their quality.'

Tom took stock of his customer. Didn't really care for this type of woman, bit too horsy and masculine—a woman should be feminine and frilly.

'What I have in mind is a pair of second-hand ones—the type made before the war.'

'You mean Parker Knowle chairs?'

'Yes, that is exactly what I do mean. I don't think they are being made now, and my only chance is to buy them second-hand from a dealer. I want green upholstery for preference, in good condition if possible, although I don't really mind if I have to pay for them to be re-covered.'

'Bit out of my line, madam. I go in for antiques.'

'Yes, I see you do, but I thought perhaps you might come across some when you go to the sales. I haven't any chance to attend them myself. With my small lounge nothing else seems suitable, and although perhaps they're not easy to find I am willing to pay a good price for them —within reason, of course.'

'What sort of price have you got in mind?' Tom was not going to

turn business away. It was out of his line but if he happened to come
across a pair there was no reason why he should not make a pound or two.
He saw this type of chair occasionally in the sale-rooms, not very often
in pairs, and they usually made about fourteen to fifteen pounds each, if
in good condition—much less if the upholstery was tatty.

'I don't really want to spend more than fifty pounds on them, but I
would go to sixty, if the upholstery was good. I just cannot afford to go
beyond that figure.'

That's all right, thought Tom, certain tenner profit there—or more.

'Very well, madam, I will keep my eyes open and see what I can do.'

'Very nice of you, Mr—er—Elliot?—that's right—you were recommended to me by a friend of mine in the town. I have only just come here
to live. This is my address—could you write it down? Please let me know
if you are able to get them. I won't go to anyone else here, but will rely
on you.'

What with the pressure of other business, Tom completely forgot all
about those chairs, till she called in again about a fortnight later and
reminded him.

The very next day he found them in Tander's sale-rooms. Only a
small sale, starting at 11 a.m., with the lots on view the same morning.

They were a nice pair, with green floral upholstery, all in good condition—just the job! There were also two antiques—a mahogany commode in original state with the old china Welsh hat inside, and a copper
fish-kettle.

The pair of chairs came on early in the sale, but by the time it started
the whole world and his wife were squeezing into the rooms. When the
auctioneer offered the pair of chairs the bidding was brisk. Tom had hopefully started with a bid of five pounds but the rostrum plucked bids from
every quarter, and thirty pounds was reached in no time. After that it
became a straight fight between Tom and the auctioneer, who was bidding
on a commission. At forty-five pounds Tom saw his twenty pounds
profit fading, but in the end he succeeded in getting the chairs for forty-
nine pounds ten shillings. He remained in the sale-room to buy the
commode, then told the porter to go up to four pounds ten shillings for
the fish-kettle later in the sale. At the same time he got him to manœuvre
the wing-chairs to the side door, also the commode, with the intention of
taking both lots away in his car. He was immediately collared by six
other dealers, all claiming the commode and wanting to have a look at the
chairs.

'Why, Tom—they're modern!'

'What you buyin' stuff like that for?'

'He's going to fake them up and sell them to a sucker.'

'As a matter of fact I've got a customer for them—just as they are—second-hand pair of modern Parker Knowles—all right, Ropey, you can give up peering at them—you're not missing anything and all your poking and prying won't make them any older. Give up, I tell you!—you're not tearing that upholstery to bits just because you want to peer inside. Give up, I say. They were bought on commission.'

His associates at last convinced, the settlement of the commode proceeded.

'Cost nine quid, and as far as I'm concerned, that's enough.'

'It'll stand a bob or two more yet, Tom.'

'Come on, don't waste time, ten bob on and over to you, Ropey!'

In the end Tom went off quite pleased, having earned eight bob in the knockout and landed the commode on to Dickie Trewen. Serve him right—teach him not to be so greedy! None of 'em really wanted the blooming thing.

He settled his account with the clerk, loaded up the pair of chairs and took them straight to the shop where he hunted on his desk for the address of his customer.

'Ah—Mrs Tuke, 16 Bowman's Way, Torminster. No telephone number. Better send a postcard—could go up round that way—snooty part of the town, wouldn't look too good, no, a postcard would be best.'

For the next few days the usual business worries claimed Tom's attention. By the fourth day he wondered why he had not received a reply to his postcard. 'Might be away or on holiday or something,' he told his wife. 'If I haven't heard by the end of the week I'll go up to Bowman's Way and find out how the wind blows.'

There was no answer to his knocking on the door of Number 16 Bowman's Way. He tried again the next day. This time the door was opened by an elderly lady. Tom removed his trilby.

'Good morning, madam. Am I right in thinking Mrs Tuke lives here? I wish to see her regarding a pair of chairs.'

The old lady gave him a keen look. 'Does she owe you anything?'

'No,' said Tom, beginning to feel a bit fluttery in the stomach. 'Is there anything wrong?'

The old lady shook her head. 'No, not exactly.' She took in paying guests, it seemed. Mrs Tuke paid a week in advance, stayed a fortnight

L

and left about a week ago. No, she'd left no forwarding address. Yes, several people had been enquiring after her whereabouts. She said something about finding another job in Tormouth.

The old lady clearly wanted to know what brought Tom to her doorstep asking for that queer Mrs Tuke, but he wasn't prepared to discuss any of his business with her. He had quite enough to think about and went straight to Tander's sale-rooms. He knew one of the partners quite well.

'Hey, Bob, give me some information, will you?'

'Sure, Tom, if I can. Don't often see you these days up at the club. What do you want to know?'

'Two weeks ago at your sale I bought a pair of wing-chairs for forty-nine pounds ten. Who put them in?'

'Oh, that's easy. Breaking the rules by telling you, and all that—let's see, this is the book . . . mm, yes, that's right. Here we are—pair of second-hand walnut wing-armchairs—Mrs Tuke, 16 Bowman's Way.'

Tom's suspicions were finally confirmed.

'Any reserve on them?'

'Yes. Forty-nine pounds. Didn't think they would sell at that price and told her so. I remember the woman well. Said she was sure they would fetch fifty pounds and quite prepared to pay our reserve charge if they didn't.'

Tom felt sick inside at the thought of having had one like that put across him.

'You've paid her the money, I suppose?'

'Oh yes—three days after the sale. She came in for it. Anything wrong?'

'No, Bob . . . thank you. It's a small world. Much obliged for the information. Just had to find out about them for somebody, that's all.'

'Old Tom didn't look too good,' said young Tander to his chief clerk.

Tom lost nineteen pounds on the chairs, and was not likely to forget it.

Willy returned home after an abortive morning at the sale to find a customer waiting for him.

'Say, are you Willy Shaun? My name's Kennedy and I come from Dallas, Texas. I took a poke round the shippers—saw some goods destined for a friend of mine. Boy, I say to myself, those are my kinda goods too, so I read the labels and see your address. There's my card—got anything more for me? I guess I can pay more than he can.'

They went into Willy's showroom and Kennedy finished by buying every small piece of oak furniture and all the country-made solid mahogany in the place.

'Saw a coupla bits of porch furniture as I came in. Wanna buy them. How much?'

Willy was puzzled for a moment.

'Yeah—porch furniture,' persisted Kennedy. 'The two painted iron seats. That lot I just bought, that'll all be painted too. Got to paint it white—looks cool.'

'Do you mean to say you are painting all this mahogany furniture?'
'Sure—got to.'

'Why don't you have it made out there? It would be much cheaper and no one would know the difference after it had all been painted.'

'Boy, you sure don't know our country. To make it noo would cost double what it costs to come over here and get it.'

'But why are you bothering about antiques? Ordinary second-hand antique-styled furniture would serve the same purpose and be a jolly sight cheaper.'

'Nah! Be dutiable for customs. Besides, our people wouldn't buy that kinda muck. It's gotta be gen-u-ine or they ain't got no interest in it.'

This was a new one on Willy but all was grist to the mill. They went out and looked at the cast-iron seats, tortured into curly-wurly pierced floral designs and heavy lion's-paw feet.

'I took them over when I bought the house. They're not really for sale. If you want them you will have to tempt me.'

'Two hundred dollars for the two and not a cent more. That's my price. I buy them cheaper most times.'

Willy whistled inwardly. Two hundred dollars? That's the best part of seventy pounds! Thirty-five pounds each? For crying out loud! What some people will pay for rubbish. Hang it all, the seats are Victorian, made some time after the Great Exhibition of 1851—shocking design in the worst possible taste. Ah well—one born every minute!

'They're yours, but they will be dutiable. I can't put them down on the invoice as being made before 1830.'

'Sure they'll be dutiable, but leave that to the shipping agent. I'll be coming round again this time next year. You buy every piece of porch furniture you can for me—anything like those seats—chairs, tables—

anything that's usable, not just ornamental. We gotta good market—so goddam' hot there that all the entertaining is done out on the porch. Cast iron stands up to the exposure and the heat. Veneered stuff just cracks up in no time. Reemember, anything to do with sleepin', sittin', and eatin'. Now, send this invoice to the shippers, keep this order form, wait till you get their instructions and you'll have your money at the same time. Send the goods up as directed. Good day to you, see you next year! O.K.' and he was gone with the usual handshake.

The whole deal had taken no longer than half an hour.

Ethel had just called him in for lunch when the phone rang.

'Hallo! Shaun speaking. Oh, hallo, Tom. You have? No good? Oh dear. What was the matter with it? Painted on a print stuck down on old canvas? Damn!—there's some swindlers about! We were too clever. Looks as if there is twenty pound each gone down the drain. *He didn't charge a fiver for cleaning it?* Rubbing it in a bit! Yes, I suppose he has got to live but a fiver is a bit thick, hang it all. I bet he only cleaned off a corner of it. We ought to have let it alone—left it good enough for someone else to have had a gamble on it. We were too greedy. Yes, I know all about looking like a Reynolds and being worth two hundred and fifty if it had been right, but what have we got for our money now—something which nobody in their right senses will ever buy. Yes, could do. Ask him to send it back to us. We'll see how much work he put in for his fiver. Yes, I agree, on second thoughts it would be a much better idea for him to give it a coat of good old dirty varnish. We could try it in another sale somewhere. The trouble is it takes such a long time for the smell of varnish to die down and if it goes into the sale-rooms smelling of fresh varnish all the dealers will shy away from it like rats from a polecat. No—you have it, Tom. Stand a much better chance in your shop—might get a private punter to have a go at it. What does that matter? . . . After all, it can't bounce back on you. Does anybody think he's going to get a genuine Reynolds portrait for forty-odd quid? Well then, tell them you are selling it on commission, say that the portrait belongs to a Mr. Shaun and they can make an offer direct to him if they like, as long as you get your commission. You know how to tell the tale. Oh sure. I don't mind losing a tenner. Better to get half our money back than have forty pounds tied up for a long time in a dud lot. That's what comes of gambling, Tom. Next time I'll leave the pictures to the picture trade and stick to what I do know something about.'

Such are the minor irritations of a dealer's day.

Willy, after returning to a warmed-up plateful of fish pie, got down to his job for the afternoon—balancing the books. And every penny of it earned the hard way, he said to himself, remembering the two contemptuous old bags in the sale-room and consigning them to the special hell he kept for Inland Revenue officials and other birds of ill-omen who, in his opinion, existed only to crab a man's initiative and intelligence and leave him stripped at the end of his hardworking life.

As for the Rockingham cottages, warnings passed from dealer to dealer, town to town, but many small dealers, back-alley merchants, and 'pretty-pretty' shops made great displays of the cottages in their windows.

Once bitten twice shy for the bigger men, so when the cottages changed to Chelsea figures, Derby Mansion House Dwarfs, and other more important specimens of porcelain, the pedlars of these pseudo-antiques found themselves up against it. The 'old aunt dying' story was dropped, and all sorts of other cunning tricks and dodges were tried, but nowhere did they meet with anything like the wonderful success they achieved with the first few loads of those Rockingham cottages. Where were they made? That for the time being remains a mystery. Some said in Devonshire or Cornwall, some said on the Continent.

13   'Did You Buy It?'

'Sales—six hundred and forty-two pounds. Profit one hundred and forty-eight. Cash to bank six hundred and forty-two less one ninety-eight for purchases and petty cash thirty-six pounds. Four hundred and eight to pay in.'

Scrutinizing several odd pieces of paper, Willy heaved a final sigh of satisfaction. After some juggling here and there he had arrived at a balance. He closed his books and stacked them in a neat pile preparatory to putting them away. Instead of doing so he propped his elbows on the desk and with face cupped in his hands sat staring into space. He could not get 'Crash' Wilson out of his thoughts.

'Crash' was reputed to be in serious trouble with the police. There had been an outbreak of theft in the district, almost always in houses which

'Crash' had lately visited in search of copper, brass, china—silver if he was lucky. He was an experienced 'tapper', good at winning a housewife's sympathy with his pathetic appealing expression and well-worn respectable clothing, and, though he didn't know the value of everything he spotted, he could give valuable information in the right quarter—mostly to one particular antique dealer who, it appeared from current rumour, was not standing by him now. As for the idea that he'd been tipping off a gang of thieves . . . 'Crash' couldn't and wouldn't have, thought Willy. I've known him for years. Or could he? Hasn't been short of money lately. Probably a very nasty coincidence. Trouble is, if they are questioning so closely as all that they may start checking up on all the people who do business with him.

An uncomfortable feeling came over Willy as he thought about his collection of silver. He had added considerably to the nucleus of fine silver kept from what he'd inherited from his father. If he were forced to do so he could account for most of it, but any undue publicity would bring the tax hounds on his track. Once they'd sunk their fangs in they never let go. The 'fiddler' has to pay for his own tune if he gets caught, he told himself. And went on, as he often found himself doing these days, to size up his situation now and in the future. Things were getting difficult.

Still no trouble to sell the right kind of stuff but it's getting so hard to find it. Wedgwood?—sell it on the phone, but where is it? Not one single piece in the sale-rooms for over six weeks. Where are all the Worcester and Derby figures, the dessert services and pairs of vases?—like Chelsea and Bow porcelain—things of the past. Some of the big firms seem to get hold of them, but at what a price! It's easy enough to sell a good item over a hundred pounds and easy to sell anything under ten, but jolly nigh impossible to sell in between. Why? I don't know. Perhaps the buyer's losing interest—money's tighter. Plenty of it in the wrong hands spent on football pools, racing, televisions in every room of their subsidized council houses. Many of them don't let the antique trade get a look-in there. All they want is gaudy, showy muck—some of it not even veneered but sprayed with cellulose and grained to look like wood. Just can't understand why they buy it. Haven't been brought up to recognize quality, I suppose. Of course they can buy a houseful of it with a down payment of a fiver. Can't sell a bow-front chest of drawers these days. Look at the three I've got in stock. Not one over thirty pounds—good chests—not too big, yet nobody wants them. Yet if I had a decent shop they would sell.

Slowly his thoughts came back to where they always returned of late
—a decent shop. There's nothing left in the knockout nowadays. If
there's anything good at a sale, everyone turns up from miles around,
forty or fifty dealers, all hoping to take home a day's work. The position
is getting impossible. Say you're lucky enough to buy a lot under the
hammer for two hundred pounds, that's worth four hundred, are you
going to be able to hold it in the ring afterwards for three hundred and
sixty to show a decent profit? Not on your Nelly! What does the knockout money amount to at that price anyway? Two hundred pounds divided
between fifty people—four pounds apiece—not worth picking up. To
get more you have to gamble, gamble with other men prepared to do the
same, perhaps up to six hundred, hoping that it won't be dropped on you.
Even then you'd only get fourteen pounds or so for a risk of a certain loss
of two hundred if you were landed with it. Just not worth while—a mug's
game, not much better than horse racing. Things have been different in
the past. I've done all right out of it—got me where I am today, but if it
goes on getting worse perhaps it would be better to change tactics.

He reached across the desk and picked up one of his trade magazines,
slowly thumbing over the pages.

He knew exactly what he wanted to look at but was in no hurry. He
stopped at a page where the corner had been turned down and which
he'd marked in pencil.

FOR SALE. Long Established Antique Business situated in a small town near
London. Fine small period Georgian house in very select quiet street, just off
Town Centre. Adjacent Court Yard with Garages, offices and large workshops
at rear. Three ground-floor showrooms and stores. Self-contained dwelling
above, comprising large lounge, dining-room, kitchen, 2 pantries, W.C. and
box room. 2nd floor, 2 large bedrooms, 2 smaller bedrooms, bathroom, sep.
W.C. Linen cupboards and box room. All bedrooms h. and c. To be Sold as a
Going Concern. T.O. approx. £28,000 p.a. Books can be inspected by approved
arrangement. Rates £120 p.a.

Freehold £15,500. All or part of stock at valuation if required. No portion
can remain on mortgage. Apply to sole agents, F. S. and T. L. & Co. Ltd.
Tel. Compton Margate 2867.

Charlie Minden's business. Poor old Charlie!

He had been a well-known figure in the antique trade. He was a good
dealer, seldom if ever in the knockout unless forced into it by sheer
weight of opposition, and with his fine judgment he could make up his

mind in seconds while others less courageous or less knowledgeable took as many minutes. Willy had always found it a pleasure to do business with him. Alert, perky, darting in and out amongst the stock, he wasted no time, asked the price, never attempted to beat you down, either bought or did not, and the deal was over, an amiable chat with news, juicy to the ears of his confrères, following with the cheque.

'Hear about the Gatton Sale? Simond got strowfed with a humdinger[1] of a French piece. The bit was coming down the hole for the maiden bid[2] when some private gent slipped inside the bidding[3] and ran it up to three hundred. Taffy was bidding. Three hundred was his limit and against him. It was just about to die in the hole[4] when Rossie, reckoning there were quite a few willing to have a gamble on it, popped over the odds and got it.

'Afterwards about ten of them had a right good go. Two got cold feet, and dropped out at a hundred on, but the other eight ran it up to five hundred on. Simond swears they were working seven-handed[5] against him. Ploughing his share back it stands him in at about seven hundred and fifty pounds. The others had something like fifty pounds apiece out of him. He will dip two fifty[6] for certain unless he can unload it privately.'

Yes. Charlie always had some news. So his wife is selling? About the only thing she can do—never took much interest in the actual business —no children. Devil of a price, fifteen thousand five hundred! That is only hoping price, of course, but even if two thousand can be knocked off it is still an awful lot of money. Never called on him, don't know what it looks like. Wouldn't do any harm to take a run over there in the car to see it. Sounds very attractive. Good area—London's snooty dormitory. Plenty of money in that quarter—just far enough out to be countrified. Wonder if it has been sold? Shouldn't think so, that sort of money isn't in everyone's bank account. The decision won't rest with me this time —have to ask Ethel and Ann. Ethel may not want to move. Had enough

---

[1] *Strowfed with a humdinger* means ending up with a very, very expensive item.

[2] *To come down the hole for the maiden bid* means to be bought under the hammer for the first bid made.

[3] *To slip inside the bidding* means to carry on bidding for a lot when someone else has nearly bought it.

[4] *To die in the hole* means that something is sold to an opponent for the exact limit of the under-bidder. For example, one might be prepared to go to twenty pounds, only to find it knocked down to the opponents for the same sum.

[5] *To work seven-handed.* Seven individuals forming themselves into a syndicate.

[6] *To dip two fifty.* To lose two hundred and fifty pounds.

[7] *To unload it privately* means sell it to a customer who is not a dealer.

ructions when I sprang this place on her, let alone moving up to London. Ann? What will she say? She'll have to do a lot of the selling. I can't face private customers again—especially lah-di-dah ones—just couldn't bring myself to do it. Buying, yes, perhaps, but not selling. She could— she's had the education, got the speech, got the manners, and a good-looking girl is an asset in any shop. She knows something about antiques, too. So she ought—moved about amongst them long enough. Wonder if she will want to move away from all her friends? Let's have a check-up again to see how I stand. Again he went through his assets. With what he had in the bank plus one or two good saleable pieces kept apart from his stock (which he'd want for the new shop) he reckoned he'd have near enough thirteen thousand.

The Big Man wants to buy the wine-cooler, and the Chippendale butterfly table ought to fetch four fifty, the pair of Regency mirrors and the pair of consoles under them six hundred for the two pairs, possibly seven fifty (poor old Mellis!—all he got was a wasted journey and a flea in his ear). And there's the house. Trouble is, I don't know what to ask for it. Have to ring up Jack. Say four thousand five hundred for the house and garden, and fifteen hundred for the field.

That brought the total to nineteen thousand—he was there and with money to spare, but all the eggs would be mostly in one basket. Comforting thought that if he made any profit on the property it couldn't be touched by the Inland Revenue—capital appreciation! He decided to slip over next day for a look round. He'd say nothing, of course, to any-one—might not be any good. Poor old Crash! he thought as he locked up his desk—can't help but it seems something is very, very wrong there. Wonder if they have a case against him yet? How on earth could one remember what one was doing three weeks ago last Tuesday? I couldn't. Let's hope they don't ask me.

It was a very different November day from the Sunday just over three years ago, when Willy had stood in his garden looking over to the moors and first seriously considered the idea of moving, of getting a shop. Now, as he left Torminster behind him and stepped on the accelerator, he was glad to switch on the heater. Crossing Salisbury Plain the wind caught the car in great buffets, yet the needle hardly wavered from a steady seventy-five. It had been raining, and as he swept down the long hill into Compton Margate the tyres threw up little spurts of water as they swished over the leaf-sodden tarmac, and through the open window he caught a whiff of

leaf-mould and wood-smoke. The little town lay spread out before him,
red and white and prosperous-looking, tame after the sharply contrasting
contours of Torminster, with a pine-covered spur of the North Downs
spread out like a protecting arm to the north, and the rolling Weald to the
south. Even at this hour there was a steady stream of cars along the by-
pass, some on their way to the coast, others filtering off into the town
itself. Couldn't be better placed, he thought.

He had no difficulty in finding the street. Charlie Minden had been a
well-known and popular citizen. He looked at his watch. Five past two—
not bad considering the distance from Torminster. There was no mis-
taking Charlie's business. The whole building, with its white-painted
façade, the red-tiled roof and all woodwork painted a light greeny-blue,
stood out a mile.

Willy took the position in. Lovely! Nice wide street—houses on
both sides all the same sort of period, one or two Victorian and gawky
but the whole street is 'class'. Don't think much of the high garden walls
of the houses opposite—bit dreary to look out on, but I expect there is
a good view of the gardens from the windows upstairs. No cramped-in
feeling. Poor old Dad!—not like ours in Torminster, eh? Bet you would
be proud to see me own a place like this. You wouldn't have been comfortable in it, though, you with your shirt, with no collar, no tie. Good
old Dad!—got a lot to be thankful to you for.

There'll be no parking problems, he thought, looking at the large
gravelled courtyard that allowed all the interesting character of the house
to be seen. Next to the house were a pair of fine Georgian wrought-iron
gates leading into the garden. Then there were the two garage doors and
near them the workshop. The garages had been converted from the old
stables and here the wall fronting the street had been built to a height
sufficient to hide completely what went on behind. There was an air of
genteel privacy about the whole place, notwithstanding the large sign
Antiques splashed across the side wall of the house in between the lower-
and first-floor windows. The courtyard walls were painted white to
match the house. Been done recently by the look of it, done up to sell!
Like the look of the gates—very attractive peep of the garden through
them. Don't care much for the shop-windows—too poky and small—
people can't see in. Don't know what could be done about them—pity
to take them out and enlarge the openings—never look the same. Looks
as if some of the original bowed glass panes are still there—can't get that
sort of glass now. I like the porch—neat and not gaudy. I like the whole

look of this place. Better get this agent fellow weighed up—sounded an
oily sort of devil on the phone. If he thinks I rang up from Torminster
this morning he'll have a shock to see me so early in the afternoon. Don't
like doing business with agents. Think I'll leave the car where I've parked
it and walk around and look at the town. Let's see now, turn to the right
at the end of this street and the next street should lead straight out into
the middle of the High Street. Yes, here we are, there's the High Street
at the bottom. Surprisingly quiet here in this quarter with the main
street so near. Ah, High Street again. Those agents should be somewhere
up the road.

On giving his name to the receptionist Willy was ushered into the
presence of the senior partner. Anything under ten thousand pounds
was relegated to the juniors.

'Mr Shaun? How do you do, sir? My name is Scurry—senior partner.
You are here earlier than I expected.'

'Fast car. I've seen the place. Want to look inside.'

His voice conveyed nothing and his face even less.

'Oh yes, certainly, quite. I will ring for the keys. Would you like
to come in my car?'

'I'd rather walk, if you have no objection. This is my first visit to the
town.'

Willy wanted to weigh up his man, and the agent also had the same
idea; the last thing either of them was going to talk about on their
walk was the possible purchase of the Minden shop.

Before they'd gone very far, Willy had made up his mind. Don't
trust that man an inch—slippery-looking blighter—London born and
bred—city slicker—run word in a minute if he had a pound more offered
for something he was selling, even though someone was signing on the
dotted line. Make him an offer and he'll squirm and wriggle, but he'll
not do a straight deal. Just the sort of man to philander and play about,
keep on stalling, hoping all the time to be able to play one interested
party off against another, forcing up the price. Shake hands with you
and then kick your backside.

Typical dealer's face, was the agent's verdict. Not giving anything
away—twisting lot, dealers. Always in a ring or something they call a
knockout designed to do the owner and the auctioneer out of their just
due. Wouldn't trust this man a yard. Country bumpkin—broad speech,
no manners. Bet he hasn't got anything like the amount of money
necessary to buy this property. Most likely wasting my time. Another of

these wretched tricksters trying to get in and buy the stock on the cheap. Just let him try, that's all. He'll get the same reception as the last one who tried that dodge.

'Here we are, sir. Would you care to go inside, or do you wish to go in through the garden gate? Mrs Minden is away, of course—with some relatives, I believe. Quite understandable. She could not possibly stay here and have all'—these dealers, he was about to say, but hastily checked himself— 'all the memories of the past brought back so vividly by the possible visits of her husband's colleagues in the trade.'

'Had many interested in it?'

This was the first relevant question Willy had asked.

'Interested? I should think we have. Twenty or so at least.'

'Why haven't you sold it before now then? Too much money? Dry rot? Or both?'

The man's no fool. Very direct in speech when he wants to be. 'Oh no. It is owing to the fact that Mrs Minden wants the money more or less straight away. I am not aware of her financial standing but she has no wish for any of the amount to remain on a mortgage.'

'Have any interested parties attempted to arrange a mortgage through the usual channels?'

'Business etiquette prevents me giving any direct answer to that question, but I believe some have.'

'Why didn't they have any success? State of building too bad or price being asked too high to appear a good risk?'

Damnation take the man! He will irritate me if he goes on questioning like this. 'It is not for me to say. Perhaps the financial position of those desiring to raise the mortgage has not been considered satisfactory.'

'As far as you know, are there any local or county council plans likely to affect the property, or the value of it, in the future?'

'No, definitely not. This part will never be scheduled for clearance— far too good a residential area. It is kept under rigid control. No new building and so on. Not that there'd necessarily be any objection if you wished to enlarge the workshop, or even wanted to build a new one. The house was acquired and converted into an antique business during the slump in the 1930's. Things are very different today. A good many local councillors have property interests in the main shopping areas, and they see to it that the value of shop properties is maintained by keeping a strict control on adjacent residential properties. A fortune is required to buy even a small shop in the High Street. Quite a number of the local

bigwigs live in this area—two of them in this street.' He waved a plump
hand. 'You see what I mean?'

Willy turned up his nose and made a face. The point was perfectly
clear—ash tubs cleared every morning, new bulbs put in the street lamps
pronto should one burn itself out, pavements swept regularly and gutters
ditto—a good thing perhaps.

'Here we are, sir. After you. That's it. What do you think of it? Mr
Minden has spent quite a lot of money on this property over the years.
This was one of his ideas.'

They were now inside, and the agent indicated the hall, or what had
once been the hall. The left and right walls had been opened into large
archways giving an immediate vista of the two large showrooms on
either side. It converted the entire ground floor facing the road into one
huge showroom. What had once been the drawing-room still retained
the original pine panelling—not wonderful, but it had been tastefully
picked out in a pale pastel-green paint. Although the windows had
appeared small from the outside, the rooms were well lit. The floor
was of polished pine strip and showed off the Persian rugs well.

Willy ran his eye over the stock. One or two very nice pieces of
furniture, otherwise nothing to shout about. Too many ormolu clocks—
not the sort of clock that sells readily nowadays. Not haphazardly bought,
any of it. Bought with an eye to the room in which it would be displayed
—clever buying, that. A thing well shown is a thing half sold. Not a
single piece of oak furniture anywhere. Don't blame him. Oak would
look all wrong in a setting of this type. If I do buy it I'll have to dump all
my oak—push it on to Tom for a tenner profit on the lot—still, all that
can wait. The layout and condition of the building is the main thing.

His companion kept up an unending patter: 'Mr Minden this, Mr
Minden that.' Willy was occupied with his own thoughts. His quick eyes
searched the floor, especially towards the walls and corners, for the tell-
tale sagging which would indicate faulty joists due to beetle or dry rot.
Every now and then, standing on one foot, he pushed downwards with
all his weight, trying to detect movement in the floor. The staircase was
a lovely feature; a half-flight of wide stairs faced the front door, then
formed a gallery for the remaining width of the hall. The second half-
flight led upwards out of sight. The balustrading was wrought iron
painted white, and a large window with arched leaded fanlight gave
adequate lighting to the staircase.

Behind the two main rooms were two smaller showrooms, reached by a passage on the left of the staircase. At one time these had been breakfast room and kitchen. Behind the kitchen were the pantries converted into a polishing-room, well equipped with work bench, two small glass-lined acid-dipping vats for cleaning dirty silver, copper, and brass, and all the necessary polishing equipment including an electric motor fitted with a huge lambswool buffer. Two more of these buffers were hanging from nails driven into the wall above the bench.

Charlie didn't like getting his hands dirty by the looks of things. I don't blame him. Acid bath is far and away the quickest and best way to clean metalware. These buffers must have cost a tenner each. Beyond was a packing-room, filled with boxes of all sizes and description, a huge stack of newspapers, sacks of straw and woodwool, and again a small bench with hammers, pincers, saws, etc., fitted into a baize-lined rack above. All very nice and handy. Outside in the out-house were the usual offices and a small store containing wood and coal.

Upstairs the living accommodation was compact. A separate outside staircase gave complete privacy from the business. Willy thought of burglars when he looked at it. The living-rooms were spacious, corresponding roughly with those below. Mrs Minden had had her own way in the kitchen. He had often seen illustrations of an English Rose kitchen. Here it was in reality. Apart from this, no great amount of money had been spent for quite a number of years. The paintwork was poor, the rooms needed re-decorating, but all were light and airy. The bedrooms on the third floor were low-ceilinged, but the best had been made of what once were the attics where the servants had their quarters.

Everywhere Willy's eyes searched for signs of decay, damp stains, woodworm, but the whole building seemed to have been well looked after. Better get Jack to give it the once-over before I really get down to business. Think I'm going to have a go at it. Looks just like what I've dreamed about for so long. As good—better in some ways—as Fred Mellis and yards ahead of Reg Bardon.

'Roof all right?'

'As far as I know it is. I have not been up to see. If you care to obtain a builder's report, there are several I can recommend.'

Willy gave a non-committal reply. All that sort of thing could come later, if necessary. Jack would have a good idea if anything was wrong up aloft.

The garden gave him his first disappointment. The peep he had of it through the wrought-iron gates had been promising, but apart from a scrubby and none-too-well-kept lawn, a weedy, gravelled path, and a large nondescript shrubbery on the other side of it planted with the idea of saving labour, there was nothing else. The back of the courtyard, where the workshop and garages were, was hidden by the overgrown shrubs, and the path seemed to disappear round in that direction.

The whole garden was surrounded by a high brick wall, a few trees on the other side discreetly hiding the neighbouring houses. The vegetable garden round behind the garages was thick with weeds. Charlie Minden had been no gardener. The agent was quick to point out that Mr Minden had been ill for some time, hence the neglect. The workshop, a long, low, brick building with a glass roof, had been converted from a greenhouse. Several cabinet-makers' benches sported electric power tools, including a bandsaw and a lathe. In a corner was an electric glue-pot. Above the benches were hundreds of various hand-tools, some now unobtainable, all neatly stored in baize-lined racks and each one labelled.

Whoever works here is a methodical man. H'm . . . smell of fresh glue. Willy sniffed again, walked over to the glue-pot and touched it. It was warm.

'Is there someone working here?'

'Oh yes, Mr Shaun, I forgot to tell you. Mr Minden employed a cabinet-maker—full time. He took in quite a large amount of antique repair work for private customers. Tom Newman's over seventy, but very active and clean at his job—he's been coming along in the mornings to finish off work that was in hand before Mr Minden died.'

Tom Newman was good news to Willy. Repair work is an antique dealer's greatest problem if he is unable to do it himself.

'That solves a problem. On an average only one piece in twenty is purchased in a proper condition to be sold to a private customer—all the rest are workshop jobs—may only be a piece of cock-beading round a drawer-edge, a chair with a loose tenon joint, or a tea-caddy with a chip from the veneer, but they all have to be done, and there are very few people left who are properly qualified to do repair work. Tom Newman is a good cabinet-maker; I can tell that without seeing any of his work. All his chisels and tools are razor sharp. I think I have seen enough. Can we go back to your office? I'm interested. I would like your permission for a friend of mine, who is also an estate agent, to come and survey it for me. Meanwhile, perhaps we can discuss the purchase price?'

An oily smile crossed the face of the agent as he inclined his head. Sleek black hair, getting thin on the top, grey at the sides, was brushed

straight back, the receding hair-line and thick black horn-rimmed spec-
tacles accentuating his somewhat narrow face into a clever-looking one.

The two of them were back in his office.

'You must understand that we have had plenty of offers, Mr Shaun—
plenty. Mrs Minden may be prepared to make a slight—er—adjustment,
but not . . .' Here he shrugged his shoulders, curled the upper lip, and
raised one eyebrow.

All the tricks of the trade, thought Willy. This is not going to be a
walkover. His eye focussed on a piece of paper, part of the contents of the
Minden file which the agent had opened and spread out on his desk.

Willy was now able to make use of a rather special accomplishment.
When he went to the Bank on Monday mornings to pay in the takings
of the previous week, there was usually a queue of people doing the same
thing, lined up at the counter. As the cashier detached the pay-in slip
and checked off the cash and cheques belonging to the customer in front,
Willy used to practise reading the slips upside down. It was surprising
how much one could learn about one's fellow townsmen in this way.

On the agent's desk was a letter, quite a short one, written to the
agent by Mrs Minden. Noticing Willy's gaze, he casually but hastily
covered all the documents with the empty cardboard file cover; but not
before Willy had taken in her signature, and the address—a small village
that he had driven through that very afternoon.

There followed a long, mostly one-sided conversation on the values
of local properties and the merits and value of the Minden one in particular.
All the agent's little points rolled off Willy like water off a duck's back,
and at last he cut in.

'If Mrs Minden is prepared to accept a lower figure, and what I consider to be a good offer, I am prepared to buy the property, subject to a
satisfactory report from my friend.' (It won't be satisfactory if Ethel or
Ann jib at coming up here, but that's none of your business!) 'May I
suggest that on a date in the near future, suitable to all parties, I meet you
here in your office, together with the owner, to see if we can bring the
purchase to a satisfactory conclusion?'

The agent was having none of this—most irregular, not in accordance
with etiquette. 'Mrs Minden is staying with relatives a long way away. We
could not expect to put her to such inconvenience when, after all, perhaps
the sale would not be concluded.'

'I would travel two or three miles quick enough if I had a chance of
selling a fourteen-thousand-pound property. As a matter of fact I think it

M

might be a good idea if I called on her to suggest it, seeing that you are so troubled about it being inconvenient for her. She is staying in Firs Road, Stickby, just outside the town; it is on my way home. I would like you to know that if we can agree upon a price I am able to pay out-right and at once. Now, sir, would you consider telephoning Mrs Minden, or shall I call to see her on my way home?'

The agent tried not to show his annoyance. He was neatly driven into a corner and knew it. He liked to make the sales his own way. The Minden property had created a lot of interest, and even though no one as yet had come up to scratch there was no reason at the moment why a deal should be made at a lower figure. It would not be the first time he had played one interested party off against another, if that other could be found. If Mrs Minden once met up with this boorish tricky dealer she might very likely reject his advice and accept an offer. However, he had not yet played all his trumps. Lifting the receiver he dialled a number.

Willy could hear the 'brr, brr, brr' but the call remained unanswered. After allowing it to ring for some time, the receiver was replaced.

'No one in. That is unfortunate. I'm sorry, Mr Shaun, I will com-municate with you as soon as I have contacted Mrs Minden. Could I have your telephone number?'

Willy gave it to him, shook hands, and departed with a large envelope containing photographs of what might well be his new business.

As soon as the office door closed behind him a broad grin appeared on the face of the estate agent.

'Takes a Londoner to make rings round these country yokels!'

Instead of dialling the telephone number of the address where Mrs Minden was staying he had dialled his own home number, knowing full well that his wife was out at one of her bridge parties. He busied himself in catching up on the routine work which his visitor had delayed, deciding not to go out for his light tea at a nearby restaurant.

At five and twenty past five his secretary brought in the usual letters requiring his signature before despatch. In the middle of signing one, the telephone rang.

'Hullo. Speaking. . . . Oh, good afternoon, Mrs Minden. I was on the point of . . . You've what? There with you now? Of all the . . . ! I do not conduct my business in that way, Mrs Minden. I know it is not sold yet but . . . If you are not satisfied, madam, with the way I am handling your business, which, of course, is mine as well, you have only to say and I will . . . No, definitely not. I don't agree. There has been far too much interest in the property to warrant doing so yet. . . . We did not discuss a price; all he said was that he would be prepared to make an offer. If any offers are to be made they should be made to me. . . . I know all about that but you are rather taking things out of my hands. . . . Yes, I suppose so. I still think it is a mistake. . . . No, of course not. Yes, it will be. . . . Very good, Mrs Minden. Thank you. Good afternoon.'

The receiver was banged down on the rest.

'Of all the dirty sneaking rats! Blast the man! Blast him! *Blast* him!'

With the speedometer continually hovering on seventy-five, the Cadillac sped homewards, its performance still as good as the day Willy had bought it, though the bodywork had seen its best years. He referred to it as his 'good old bus' and had no intention of parting with it in a hurry.

Arriving home just after 10.30 p.m., he smelt Lancashire hotpot even while putting the car away in the garage. Ethel, hearing him arrive, had the steaming casserole ready for him on the table.

'Hallo, dear,' he said. 'Sorry I'm a bit late. My, that looks good.'

'Did you buy it?'

The question did not make immediate sense to her husband.

'Did I buy what?'

'The property you went nearly up to London to look at today.'

Willy saw the twinkle in her eye and laughed out loud.

'How on earth do you know what I have been doing? Not one word about it has passed my lips. Somebody telephone?'

Ethel shook her head. While she was tidying up in the office she had come across the trade magazine with the page-corner turned down; the dog-eared page was too much for her curiosity, and the pencil cross in the margin soon told her all she wanted to know.

'Well, did you buy it, I said.'

Already seated with his mouth full of dumpling, onion, and carrot, Willy shook his head.

'No,' he said at length. 'Not yet, dear. There is a lot to talk over. The property is good as far as I can judge.'

'Talk things over! That's more than you did last time.' Ethel could not refrain from getting in that one.

'We've been over that too many times, dear. Looking back, can you say I made a mistake?'

'That's not the point, and anyway, what is this new place like?'

She lapped up the details, pressing for more.

'How on earth do you expect me to know the colour of the curtains Mrs Minden had in the lounge? I was more concerned with the state of the building. By the way, I must see Jack Earnshalle tomorrow morning. We've had some good years here dear, good years, but, apart from other reasons, this kind of business will not hold much longer—another five or ten years, perhaps. I would rather get out sooner on my own accord than be forced out later. What about coming with us when Jack goes up to vet it for me? Perhaps his wife would come—make a real day of it. What about Ann? Think she will want to leave Torminster?'

'She's as ready to leave as I am. Oh, don't think I'm grumbling, but I'm a bit fed up with living out here in the country. There is enough to do, more than enough, but it is so isolated—no life—no company. I know I have the Women's Institute, the Church work, and all that; and Ann has made quite a number of friends in the district. But things have not turned out how I once imagined they would.'

Willy nodded, vaguely aware of what his wife meant, but he made no comment. Snobbery was far greater in the villages, with their Manors, Halls, Courts, Lodges, and Houses, than in the town, where it was only a question of being able to keep up with the Joneses.

'It's a lot of money.'

'Can you buy it any less?'

'I hope so. I'm very taken with it. It is just off the main shopping centre in a rather toffee-nosed residential district. There's a photograph of it.'

'Oooh, lovely! If you're hard pressed you're welcome to all my nest egg.'

The Women's Institute had an organization for selling all surplus vegetables, jars of home-made jam, bottled fruit and pickles, honey, flowers, and even home-made rugs. Ethel had not been slow to take advantage of it. The kitchen garden produced about ten times more than the three of them required. Ruling Elkins, who was allowed to take home whatever he wanted, and the garden, Ethel had a nice fat little sum of money tucked away.

Willy laughed. 'Thanks, darling, but I could buy it outright now and still have some left over, that is if this property can be sold quickly. I want to talk things over with Jack tomorrow. '

14 'Going . . . going . . .'

The next morning Ann was too excited to eat her breakfast. Her mother had given her all the details and told her that a lot depended on whether she was prepared to do the selling of the antiques in the showrooms. She realized that she would miss a good many of her friends but oh, what a relief to get away from that stuffy solicitor's office! To be near London was to be near life and bustle, and she would meet hundreds and hundreds of people instead of the same daily three or four. Room for a tennis court in the garden—that made her happy! Plenty of tennis and dancing—her two favourite pastimes. London, London, here I come!

By this time Willy was already in Torminster, having called on Tom to ask him to stand in for him at a sale and left the car at his garage to have it serviced after the long run of the day before and ready to go back.

Now he and Jack Earnshalle were in the latter's private office.

'Sounds a bit on the steep side to me, Will. Still, I don't think you could go wrong, not from the description. The district counts quite a bit. Anyway, we will get down in a huddle after I've had a look at it. Now, about your place. I'm going to charge you, mind, but boy! I'm going to town on those five acres of yours. I have been on the point of telephoning you dozens of times during the last fortnight. I was only saying to the wife a few months ago that I didn't give you much longer in Torminster. We hear a thing or two, you know. Done pretty well for yourself one way and another.'

'Some bank clerk been opening his mouth by the sound of it. I'll give the manager a rouser.'

'Forget it. What do you expect to get for the property?'

Willy thought for a minute, then named a sum five hundred in excess of the sum he had in mind.

Jack clapped his hands.

'Ha! We've been friends for a long time, lad—too long for me to do the dirty on you. There are quite a few who would sell it for you at that sum—sell it to themselves. You'd know nothing about it but that's what would happen. You would be the sucker and they would get the pickings. Are you going to let me sell it for you?'

'That's the idea of it, Jack. I have always relied on you before.'

'I'm not going to charge the usual commission, mind you. This is strictly business. I want ten per cent of the selling price and don't you breathe a word about it. If we belong to the union, as it were, we are supposed to stick to the scale of charges as laid down by them.'

Willy frowned. 'Bit steep isn't it?'

'Not for what I have up my sleeve. You go to someone else and you'll get diddled.'

'All right, Jack—it's a deal. I wouldn't trust some of the sharpers in your trade in this town any further than I could throw them. Now what have you got up your sleeve?'

'Let's examine your property together and I'll try to put you in the picture. In the first place, there are five acres of land more or less uncontrolled. I believe you let the grazing to old Tansmeed after young Madden gave up keeping pigs? He pays you monthly and the agreement can be terminated either side by a month's notice. Correct?'

'That's right, but how did you know that?'

Jack waved the question aside.

'You've got farm land all round you—two huge estates, both entailed

—entail can't be broken—the land can't be sold. You own the only decent-sized plot of freehold ground in your district apart from a few properties in the village itself.'

'I suppose you've got some builder waiting for it? I've had one or two approach me with the idea, I suppose, of turning it into a housing site.'

'Yes, as a matter of fact I have, Willy: three of them.' And Jack went into a detailed account of the private hopes, schemes, and long-term machinations of those three builders which made Willy sit back listening in amazement.

'How on earth do you know all this?'

Jack gave him a shrewd look.

'Outsiders think you just buy and sell antiques. I don't know much about your side of the business but I do know there's far more to it than just buying and selling, there's far more to it than that. It's the same with an estate agent. It's not just a matter of sticking a "For Sale" board in somebody's garden, perhaps arrange a mortgage, complete the contract, draw your commission and take the sign down again. No, sir! In this game you have to be well into the future, know everybody's business and be a jump ahead of your rivals. I know what I know, and it is no odds to anyone how I get my information. What is that land worth as a building site? No more than two thousand five hundred, but we could squeeze another five hundred out of one or other of them.'

'That sounds all right to me, Jack—more than I anticipated, but what about the house itself?'

'I'm coming to that. The house on its own should fetch three thousand seven hundred and fifty, but those builder chappies have one in the eye coming to them if I am successful. Your five acres have another value, something you could not have been expected to know. I'm not saying that there is oil underneath, but how near or far away is your nearest neighbour?'

The question seemed a silly one. Willy was stumped for a minute.

'My nearest neighbours? There's the pair of tumbledown cottages along the road about three hundred yards away. They're condemned—due to be pulled down sometime this year. I heard that the estate were not going to rebuild.'

'Quite correct. I know all about those cottages. Not counting them, how far to the next neighbour?'

'A good quarter of a mile in that case.'

'Just so. Your five acres are nearly unique in this part of the world, the moors excepted. A London estate office has just put out a broadcast: "Five to ten acres of land wanted, somewhere in this area." Not prepared to state what they are wanted for, but they must have a habitation clearance of at least a quarter of a mile. They must be acting for some big concern —my guess is something to do with new kinds of fuels or explosives. Perhaps they want to test out on the moors what they will be making. Who knows? The land has to be fairly near a source of skilled and semi-skilled building labour. Twenty miles stipulated; obviously some major building operations. Water and electricity—you have both right on the land. That's worth a pound or so. Ever since I heard about this I have been round and round the county—only two other possible properties and neither could be bought for love or money. A half-mile diameter habitation clearance is asking for something with labour, water, and electricity thrown in. I've had a good scout round your place, you may be sure. I'd've had to come to you outright sooner or later but if I had it's doubtful if I could have bargained for my ten per cent.'

'You've no idea who it is?'

'Not really.'

'In that case they can jolly well afford to pay. Now what is the property worth?'

'As much as we can get, but it is no good sticking it on too hard. They know when someone is trying to twist their tail. It's better to ask a steep price which is within reason and get it, than to ask the impossible and end up with less than you could have got in the first place. Let us say twelve thousand five hundred and not take less than ten. It will be a good day's work if we pull it off. Can I go ahead?'

'You sure can, Jack. Ten per cent as agreed. Anyone could have twisted that property out of me for six thousand. If you do sell it, how long is everything going to take before the money comes?'

'Just as soon as it's sold, boy, and not before.

'Hallo, operator, I want a London number . . .'

He put his hand on the mouth-piece. 'If you want any money mean-while I'll fix you up, even if I have to lend it to you myself.'

Interesting, thought Willy. He could never fathom Jack's financial standing but he obviously had a few thousand or so which he could put his hand on straight away.

'Hallo! Is that Gabber and Whetstone? Could I speak to Mr. Whet-stone, please? This is Earnshalle, estate agent of Torminster. . . . Look, this is urgent, a long-distance call and a very expensive one. . . . I see. Thank you very much. Hallo. That Mr Whetstone? Good morning. Earnshalle of Torminster here. About the letter you sent regarding the purchase of some land in this area. Yes, that's right. Not cancelled, is it? . . . You are? . . . Good! I've got it.' Jack winked at Willy. 'Fifteen miles outside of Torminster. Five acres and a bit. Complies with all stipulations. Electricity and water right on the doorstep. Yes, I think so . . . positive. No, not low lying—well above water level. . . . Yes, quite flat . . . well, rises a bit at one end but not much. . . . Sorry, can't answer that. . . . Well over a quarter of a mile away. . . . Within a month if you want it that soon. . . . Fourteen thousand.' Jack winked at Willy again. 'I don't think so. The builders are after it. . . . The only one round here for miles. . . . Good house there, too. Make good office accommodation or the house for the manager. . . . No. I don't know what the land is wanted for. How could I know? Just guessed there would be some kind of building going on. . . . No, I know it isn't any of my business. . . . Keep your wool on, old man . . . no offence meant. No. He is a friend of mine and that makes things awkward. . . . Well, say twelve seven fifty to him and all extras forward your end, including my commission. . . . No, I cannot do that. I told you, he is a friend of mine—commission will have to come from you. . . . You will? That's very good of you. . . . Yes. Here? . . . Oh yes. He will be here too. . . . Right. . . . Thank you very much. Goodbye.'

Jack put down the receiver. 'Sold!' was all he said.

Willy looked at him with mouth slightly open and a vacant expression. 'Did you say "sold"?'

'Yes, lad, sold, subject to an examination by Gabber's surveyor and two surveyors working for their clients. They want to take certain soil tests. I put my head into a hornets' nest about "building something on it", but they asked me if I knew what sort of formation is underneath the top soil. You got any idea?'

'Clay, then rock, I think. Elkins said there was a lot of clay, once.'

'All four of them will be here tomorrow—Whetstone and the three surveyors. Two of them will be coming down from up north somewhere so the appointment is fixed for 3 p.m. tomorrow. You will be home waiting for us just after that? These chaps don't lose much time.'

'Yes, I'll be there. By the way, Jack, you seem to have managed to dig some more commission out of the deal.'

'Do you blame me? Not that what they dole out will amount to all that much. One per cent, if I'm lucky.'

N

'No, I can't say that I blame you. Nothing like being honest while you are being crooked. Did they give you any idea who the interested party is?'

'No. I got told to mind my own business and keep my mouth shut, and we had both better do just that. An untimely word now could bring other interested parties down on us like a pack of howling wolves. What happens after we've shot our bolts doesn't matter, but until then, not a word. Much as I like your wife and daughter—not even to them, mind.'

With the words 'twelve thousand seven fifty—sold' ringing in his ears, Willy trod on air all the way home. Funny thing—Luck! He worked, he toiled and he sweated, but all that effort over the past years had not produced as much in financial gain as had the sale of his two properties, and he knew nothing about property.

Good old Jack! At last I know someone who I can call a friend, even though he is getting a fair picking out of the deal. If this comes off there will be no need to touch my working capital to any great extent. Shall have a few expenses though, moving, re-decorating, and his commission.

Next day two cars drew up in Willy's drive, and five white-coated men stepped out, among them Jack himself. One car contained drilling machinery.

'What's the big idea?' Willy asked when Jack had introduced his opposite number, Whetstone, and they went out into the fields.

'Not my idea, Will. Whetstone's idea. Even brought one down for me to wear. Didn't you read the notices on the cars? Plastered on the wind-screens and rear windows: "Hinds Farming Projects Incorporated. Biological Department".'

'These bods aren't scientist wallahs, are they?'

'No. Nothing to do with anything. Whetstone told me they usually resort to this sort of thing if any acquisition has to be kept quiet. Puts people off the scent. Five or six men prowling about your field doing peculiar things are bound to attract attention. Ten to one it will be all round the village by tonight. If anyone asks you questions, samples of soil were being taken for analysis—swine fever and all that, as you are contemplating pedigree pig-breeding. You know what a howl the farmers raise when any agricultural land is put to another use—even if the land isn't theirs.'

Nearly three hours later the surveyors came back to the house, measured up the garden, gave the buildings a quick examination, held a lengthy conversation with Whetstone, shook hands with Jack and Willy, stood in the road looking round in all directions across the fields, climbed into their car and departed. Willy held his breath. To be or not to be?

Whetstone cleared his throat.

'Er—gentlemen—er—Mr Shaun...Mr Earnshalle...my clients will purchase the property. The price was agreed yesterday.'

He handed Willy a card.

'This firm of solicitors will be acting for my clients. Will you instruct your solicitors to get in touch with them? May I have the name and address of yours? We wish this purchase to be concluded with all possible haste. Would you impress upon them the need for urgency and also for secrecy? You will be hearing from us shortly, Mr. Earnshalle. It has been nice meeting you, Mr Shaun—pleasure to do business. Thank you, gentlemen. Good afternoon, or evening, should I say?'

He joined his colleague awaiting him in the back seat of a large chauffeur-driven Humber. Willy chuckled when he saw the printed notices.

'You have to hand it to them, Jack. They know what they want and know how to set about it—Biological Department—my, that's rich! But what about the local council—how will they get past them with their plans?'

'That won't be our worry, lad. Let them fight it out between themselves. If you ask me, I think all arrangements will be made at higher levels. The little local tin gods, full of their own importance, will have to be good little boys and do what they are told. I think there will be more building under the ground than on the surface.'

'You know anything, Jack?'

'Not with any certainty. Just a guess. Anyway, we've sold it—that's the main thing.'

'What was all that about?' Ethel was waiting for her husband in the hall. 'Why don't you tell me what's going on? Were they vets, or something? Did Jack Earnshalle bring them over?'

'Yes, in a way he did, dear. We have sold the property.'

'Sold it? Who to?'

'That bunch of surveyors, acting for a client. We don't know who the client is, but we've sold it, house and fields together.'

'How much?'

'The actual figure has not been worked out yet, but it will be quite a bit more than we paid for it.'

'You're not saying much! Don't you want to talk about it?'

'No, not yet, dear. Both Jack and I gave an undertaking that we wouldn't.'

'Oh dear! I shall be sorry to leave now that I know we have got to go. This has been the first real home we ever had.' Sniff! Ethel started to cry.

'Better go and make yourself a cup of tea.'

Women! They seemed to enjoy working themselves up and having a good sentimental howl. Had he any sentiment about leaving? No, he decided. I don't think I have. The place has served its purpose. Buying it was a step forward in the right direction. Buying Charlie Minden's will be another one, and probably the last I shall take.

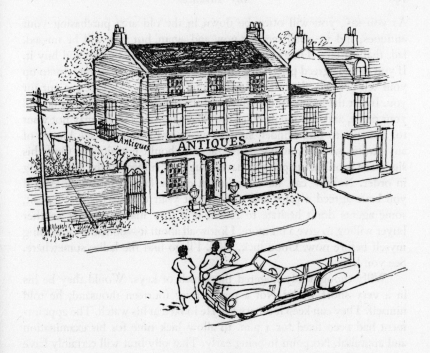

15 'Gone'

'Don't you go and mess this deal up by beating down too hard. The property is worth every penny they are asking. Not easy selling, mind. That sort of money doesn't grow on trees, but it is quality you are buying —quality. That building, God willing, will still be standing three hundred years from hence. The right position, too—snob value. If you can get it for fourteen thousand you can't go wrong. . . .'

Jack and Willy were in Compton Margate, standing on the other side of the street looking at the late Charlie Minden's shop.

Ethel and Mrs. Earnshalle, having had their fill of inspection, had been packed off to a nearby tea-room while the men got down to brass tacks.

'There's nothing wrong anywhere. If the town centre expands, as it will almost certainly have to do one day, then you or yours will be sitting on a good frontage and an even better depth. Buy it and good luck to you.

As you say, you will often be down in the old area purchasing your antiques, and we shall see you now and again, but you will be missed, lad, that's a fact. Time's getting on. You go into that office and buy it. If you get an agreed price with the owner in front of the agent, stump up your ten per cent deposit and make him sign this. I've typed it out for you. Insert the names of the street and the town, her name, his name and your name, and also the price agreed. Make him sign it. He may not want to. Show it to Mrs Minden straight away and ask her if she knows of any reason why he, acting as her agent, should not sign it. Once his signature is on that paper you have bought it, subject to the deeds being in order. Nohow can he wriggle out of the deal. Sometimes, even if you have agreed a price and written out your cheque for the deposit, some agents don't hesitate to return it if they manage to get another buyer willing to give a bit more. I know all about it—done the same thing myself before now. Good luck, Will. I'll go find the ladies somewhere. See you later.'

Willy thoughtfully fingered the bunch of keys. Would they be his in a very short while? Not a penny over fourteen thousand, he told himself. They can keep it otherwise. He looked at his watch. The appointment had been fixed for 4 p.m. to allow Jack time for his examination and appraisal. No point in being early. That oily brat will certainly have given Mrs Minden a good briefing. Be a good idea to hold back for five minutes or so—make them feel uncomfortable, sitting around.

An hour later an impasse had been reached, Willy at thirteen thousand five hundred pounds opposing fourteen thousand five hundred. Arguments for and against were bandied to and fro across the desk.

'That is the lowest figure, Mr Shaun. Lower than that we will not go. The property, the situation, the business as a going concern and the goodwill are worth every penny.'

Willy had been patiently and hopefully waiting for that word 'Goodwill'. He pounced.

'Goodwill? Did you say goodwill? You may know a considerable amount regarding the buying and selling of properties—it's your job after all—but may I say that you know very little about the nature of an antique business? The goodwill attached to the business of Charles Minden died with Charles Minden. As far as any established customers were concerned, there was and could be only one Charlie Minden.'

Mrs Minden nodded, and smiled a little. She appreciated the compliment to her late husband.

'The faith and trust which an antique dealer establishes with his customers,' he went on, 'cannot be passed on to the stranger who acquires his business. With a grocer or suchlike, yes—goodwill means a book list of customers who, unless they receive poor service, rotten goods, or both, will remain as customers. That is not so with an antique business. A moment ago you included "Goodwill" as an asset. I am sure Mrs Minden will agree with what I have said. I ask you to readjust your final price and I will make one last attempt to purchase. Fourteen thousand and I'm finished. I will leave you for a little while to talk things over.'

Willy was out of the door before the agent could say no. On returning a few minutes later he noticed that Mrs Minden's eyes were red. She was nervously sick of the whole thing. She wanted money urgently. Charlie Minden by outward appearances had been a wealthy man, but though he had made a small fortune out of antiques he had lost it again through gambling on the Stock Exchange. The early 1930's gave him a blow from which he did not fully recover until the boom in the late 1940's. This man Shaun had known her husband well, he had not made a silly offer, and he had intimated that he was willing to purchase most, if not all, of the stock. He could apparently pay for everything without delay. She had insisted on accepting his offer.

Willy heard the verdict, thanked them, and shook hands.

'That's settled, then.' He filled in the blanks on his document and handed it across the desk. 'As the sale has now been agreed between us all, you will have no objection to signing that in the presence of Mrs Minden?'

The agent read it through. A peculiar expression came over his face. In the whole of his business career he had never been asked to sign a document of that nature. It was an insult—a downright insult.

'I'm not going to sign a document of that na——' the words died on his lips as he felt the shrewd eyes boring into his, noted the widening of the nostrils and the thinning of the lips.

'—Most irregular. Your opinion of me must be very low, Mr Shaun. You realize the implications of this document? They are an insult to my integrity.'

'No offence meant, sir. Business to me is business. I have lived long enough not to trust anyone until I know they can be trusted. Would you sign it, please, and get one of your staff to witness the signatures?'

Willy pocketed a document which would give him damages, or rather 'an agreed sum for loss of interest should the agent, etc., etc.'.

'Now! About the stock. You are handling that for Mrs Minden?'

The agent nodded, anticipating another battle.

'I will take it at book value—all of it, on two conditions. The first that all items listed in the stock-book as being in stock are included and are present in the stock. The second, that the price for every item held in stock for longer than a year shall be reduced by twenty-five per cent per annum for each year the item has been in stock, irrespective of any other write-down which may have been made. I am sure that there are one or two "old friends". I have a few in my own stock, and this will enable me to get rid of the stickers without perhaps having to lose money on them.'

This was a pleasant surprise. Now knowing the kind of man with whom he was dealing the agent had been expecting a haggle over nearly every item. He had not been looking forward to this part of the transaction, for his knowledge of antiques and their values was very limited. This offer was excellent and the demand for the twenty-five per cent per annum reduction was understandable. It would give Shaun, as he said, a chance to get rid of the white elephants.

'Shall I leave you again to talk it over with Mrs Minden?'

'I don't think that will be necessary. Do you, Mrs Minden? I think you have made a very fair offer.'

Mrs Minden nodded. Both had feared that any new owner would not want some or even any of the stock. This would have entailed all the fuss and bother of selling it off privately by tender or by auction.

'Very good, Mr Shaun. Excellent. We will accept your offer, with proper regard to your conditions.'

'As to the first one, don't worry too much if a few small minor items are unaccountable. It's very rare for an antique dealer with a shop to go the whole year without getting a few things swiped; you don't notice the loss until a customer makes a particular request. Yes, I know all about *that*, and I expect Mrs Minden does too.'

Willy cut short her thankful agreement by producing his cheque-book.

'When I buy antiques I pay for them. This is to show earnest. There —three thousand pounds, and after you have checked on the stock and worked out the agreed reductions, if any, we can adjust the balance either way. Let me have a duplicate copy of the stock, together with all the prices showing the readjustments as and where they occur. Would you also check the actual stock with the stock-book? If you have any difficulty doing that, leave it until next week, when we can go over it together if necessary. Meanwhile if you could let me have the other in the post tomorrow night I would be much obliged. Give me a receipt—"on account three thousand for the complete antique stock of the late etc. etc. as shown to be in stock as per the current stock-book".'

At last there followed a general shaking of hands in a much friendlier atmosphere. Willy was quick to appreciate the change in the manner of the estate agent. They had got each other's measure and, the Minden business now almost complete, William Shaun was going to be a neighbour in the town—perhaps a man with whom business could be done to mutual advantage.

It was much too late to get any tea, so he made his way to where the car was parked.

Lovely premises. My premises now. He laughed out loud when he thought about his purchase of the stock. His quick eyes had noted the pieces of furniture upstairs in the private rooms and their value had been appraised. Like most antique dealers living above their own show-rooms, Charlie Minden had succumbed to the temptation of taking the finest pieces upstairs, ostensibly to get them out of the way of other antique dealers but really to enjoy living with the finest for a while. Such treasures as these, once upstairs, usually remained unsold until something even better was carried up to take their place. Forming part of the stock they were listed in the stock-book, perhaps year after year. Willy himself was doing the same thing. All his finest pieces of furniture were hidden away from the eyes of the trade, but were all for sale, provided any buyer was prepared to pay a very fancy price. A quick inspection of the Minden stock-book had shown him that all the furniture upstairs was held in stock and that five or six of the finest pieces had been in stock for many years. The lovely miniature Sheraton period satinwood drum-table by the window in the upstairs lounge was of seventeen years' standing, and was listed at thirty-five pounds—the original purchase price. By his arrangement he would get possession of it for about one pound ten shillings and today's value was somewhere in the region of two hundred and fifty pounds. There was also a fine Louis Quinze Bureau Plat, a pair of Hepplewhite window seats, a pair of Blue John vases with silver gilt mounts which looked like the work of Matthew Boulton, a satinwood sofa-table of fine workmanship and proportions, a tiny Sheraton period secretaire bookcase, veneered with satinwood and amboyna, and with original silver handles. (Later he discovered a maker's label in this piece—probably known to Charlie Minden, but not to him until several months after he had moved in.)

The following week he and the agent checked over the stock together. As he had foretold, one or two things proved to be missing. The agent was upset, but Willy shrugged his shoulders.

'It's neither here nor there. By the way, I would appreciate it if you could do something for me—I will pay any charges involved. I think that the items shown in the stock-book which at the moment are upstairs should be brought down here to keep everything together. Perhaps you could arrange to have that done? The odds and ends which are in the drawers of the pieces upstairs could all be put in one of the bedrooms, in readiness for Mrs Minden to take away. I understand she is not living here, but with her relatives, so I don't think she would object. The door at the top of the stairs could then be locked and the key retained by you. Mrs Minden has her own private staircase to the flat which she and the persons removing her possessions can use. This will keep all my stock away from pilfering hands. I don't want to lose any more of it—not that Mrs Minden would take anything, but I myself have often bought things from removal men without questioning them too closely as to how they came by them. And there are the local tradesmen. If anyone *has* to use the main front door, perhaps it could be opened when you were there?'

The agent thought this was a good idea. He was now more or less responsible for the stock and had no wish for anything else to be stolen. Shaun had been very sporty over the few items missing.

The final stock value, with all agreed reductions, had totalled three thousand one hundred and eight pounds ten shillings. Willy had paid the balance by return of post and had already received a receipted detailed invoice of the entire stock. The important goods upstairs he valued at well over two thousand pounds, but had been able to acquire them for a little under three hundred.

Within three weeks the sale of his own property was complete. He paid Jack his ten per cent commission by cheque and demanded a receipt. Jack looked sorrowful. 'Going to break my heart to put this cheque into the bank. Think of all the income tax I will have to pay on it! Let's forget the twelve-seventy-five and say a straight thousand pounds cash?'

With a shake of his head Willy declined.

'Sorry, old man. I haven't got anything like that amount floating these days, and besides, I'm not going to fly my flag in the face of Providence twice. I did it once before when I bought my place from Vestere. You remember? This time I can't afford to take any risks. I got away with it then but I have far more to lose now if I should happen to be caught out. I'm not running the risk of putting my head into a hornets' nest for the sake of two hundred and seventy five quid.'

Not a word leaked out regarding the sale of his property and business was carried on as usual. It had been agreed that he could remain in possession for three months to give him time to get the purchase of his new property settled.

The following weeks were very busy ones. The removal had to be arranged, new billheads printed, together with visiting cards and change-of-address postcards. This had to be done in Barston, otherwise the secret would have leaked out. Ann gave in her notice and agreed to remain at the office for a month to teach the new secretary the office routine. Willy carried on his usual round of sales, although his heart and mind were all the time elsewhere.

'What's the matter with you, Willy—losing your grip or something? You're going about like a man in a dream.' This was Tom at his elbow. Good old Tom! Willy remembered the days gone by. The plotting, the scheming they had done together. He would miss Tom more than anyone. Poor old Tom. Fine judge of furniture but lacks pluck and the courage of his convictions. He will miss me in the knockout. Can't think why he hasn't done better for himself. He has made good money. His overheads can't be all that steep, yet he doesn't seem to progress.

Had Willy been aware of the contents of the parcels neatly wrapped with brown paper and string, one of which Tom seemed perpetually to have on the rear seat of his old car, and which, unbeknown to his friends, he used to dump in bramble thickets, he would have had his last question answered: Tom's wife was an alcoholic. She had been away several times for curative treatment, but without prolonged success, which was the reason for Tom's frequent 'Gone to stay with her relatives for a while' when asked how his wife was; also for his shabby appearance at times, the grubby shirt and collar and the closed shop when he was at the sales, or out on other business. He bore his cross well. No person in Torminster, apart from the doctor, knew or suspected anything.

Meanwhile a storm was raging in the Minden quarter. Mrs Minden had visited the agent to express her concern regarding the removal of some of her furniture. What had happened to it? Her consternation changed to alarm, then anger, when it was explained to her that the furniture formed part of the stock sold to Mr Shaun and was now down-stairs with the rest. She stoutly declared that they belonged to her and that she wanted them put back immediately. These things had never been for sale—no question about that. The agent patiently pointed out that the pieces taken downstairs were held in stock, as shown by the stock-book, and that some of them had been listed year after year at the original purchase price for many years. Mrs Minden at last realized what had happened. She was furious.

'I have lived with all those things for years. Of course I must have them back. I had no idea that he was under the impression he was buying them. They are just not for sale.'

The agent was very patient, but also very firm. He was beginning to respect very much the business acumen of one William Shaun, Esq. The very pieces that gentleman had purchased for a fraction of the original cost, owing to the agreement of twenty-five per cent per annum reduction, were the most valuable in the whole collection. However, there was nothing he could do about it. The entire stock had been sold and paid for.

'It's no good, Mrs Minden. I can understand that the removal of the furniture which you considered to be yours has come as a shock, but there is nothing we can do about it.'

It had been a shock to him too. Not being very well up in antiques, he had not realized quite what was going on.

'I won't sell the property to him. He's a swindler. You can cancel everything!'

But in the end she reconciled herself to the loss of her husband's treasured possessions, and took the agent's point that she might not have done so badly after all by selling the stock as a whole, rather than by auction, with all its uncertainty, and a minimum of fifteen per cent com-mission to pay. All the same, she gave the agent to understand that she considered herself the victim of sharp practice and did not wish to meet the new owner again under any circumstances. She shortly placed her signature on the conveyance which her solicitor sent to her and that was that.

Down in Torminster, two days before the removal, Willy called on his so-called friends in the trade. There was no sale anywhere near by and he was able to find most of them in their own or each other's shops. He dropped his bombshell.

'Leaving?'

'The day after tomorrow?'

'Bought Charlie Minden's business?'

He was quick to note the incredulous expressions changing to envy and jealousy—expressions which were quickly hidden under an avalanche of insincere 'jolly good lucks', 'hope you do wells', and 'well I never, all the best, old boys'.

Willy couldn't forget the look on Tom's face when he gave him the news.

'Leaving? You? That's a blow to me, Willy. We relied on each other quite a bit. It won't be the same around here without you. I understand why you had to keep it quiet; no need to apologize. Charlie Minden's business, eh? That's a good step up the ladder. Come down here and buy me out as often as you like. Good luck to you, Willy!'

Tom was the only one who meant what he wished. Slowly the two shook hands, old memories flooding in. Neither could bring himself to speak, and each turned quickly away—Willy with the never-to-be-forgotten picture of the puzzled despair which had settled on Tom's face.

Old Tom's breaking up, he thought. When I come down I'll buy all I can from him, even if I'm not able to see much of a profit on some of it. Pity his wife was out. Would have liked to have said goodbye to her—haven't seen her for ages.

At last everything was ready. Electricity authorities notified to disconnect the supply early on the morning of the departure, Post Office—telephone ditto, all the tradesmen's bills settled up—just one more half-pint of milk to come. Ethel was worrying here, worrying there, collecting and packing isolated oddments. Ann, elated, excited, shed no tears when the faithful Bobby Cox called during the last afternoon to say goodbye. Ethel, Willy, and Ann all stood together in the front porch and watched the three great pantechnicons roll down the drive—stock-in-trade, tools, household effects, everything on board except the kitchen sink, the throw-outs, and the rubbish. The vans were going back to the depot in Tormouth, where fresh crews would take over and the vans depart about 10 p.m. for the long overnight journey towards London.

The Shaun family were all going out to dinner, Ethel and Ann staying on at the hotel for the night and catching the early-morning express train up to London. Willy, leaving just after midnight by car, aimed to breakfast somewhere en route and be outside the new home ready to supervise the unloading of the vans when they arrived.

While his wife and daughter were inside the house taking a last look round Willy had a final stroll outside. A few regrets invaded his thoughts, but the place had served its purpose. Sentiment must not be allowed to enter into a business transaction. He viewed the pile of discards and assorted rubbish by the side of the garage—old kitchen utensils, pots, pans, jam-jars, empty sherry and whisky bottles, bundles of worn clothing and household linen, rusty garden tools, flower-pots, three rolls of wire netting, piles of newspapers, odd vases, moulded glass and bits of modern pottery—some cracked, some perfect—his two oldest suits, a good sound kitchen table too big for the new home, a procession of the family's worn-out shoes, a pair of Wellington boots which let in the water—hundreds of things including a pillow which had burst whilst being tied up with others in a bundle. The wind was already playing tricks with the feathers.

He had made arrangements with a junk dealer in Torminster to collect everything on the heap; he could have the lot on the understanding that he left nothing behind.

With lower jaw out-thrust, making the wrinkles and lines more pronounced and giving him the appearance of a much older man than he was, Willy regarded that pile of throwaways. His mind recalled the pictures of many years ago. It had been out of heaps such as this that his father and he had made a living in the early days. Just the same—given to his father for nothing, provided he took it all away. Hard days, those. A twenty-mile trek out of Torminster with the old hand-cart was all in a day's work. Once again he could see his father out in the front between the shafts of the cart, wearing a dirty striped flannel shirt, without a collar, sleeves rolled up, a pair of dark blue naval officer's trousers, found in a bundle of rags, held in position by a brown leather belt polished by the sweat from his arms, a pair of stout hobnail-studded black boots, well dubbined to keep out the water, grating away on the rough-stoned road with every visible muscle and sinew standing out like whipcord as he pulled and strained between the shafts, uphill, downhill, taking home a load of something which was worth a shilling or so. He himself, about six years old, perhaps not even that, plodding on steadily behind, his bare feet rubbing in boots too big for him, pushing with all his little strength when it came to going uphill and holding on to the tailboard of the cart and letting himself be pulled along going down.

Time had turned the wheel a full cycle. It was his turn now to give stuff away—rubbish, unwanted, out of which some other poor devil would make a shilling or two. I've come a long way since then, he thought. If anything happens to me now, Ethel and Ann will be all right. The property I've just bought will always be worth money. They would have enough to live on, anyway. He knew that queer things happen to men whose work is exacting and uncertain, with long, irregular hours and snatched meals. Duodenals, coronaries—an occupational risk.

There were sounds of sniffing from the back seat when the car edged out into the road, turning to the right for Torminster. Ethel firmly believed in tearful farewells.

On the corner where the village lane met the main road stood Elkins. He had been waiting there for over an hour, to wave goodbye to a good employer whose parting shot of ten crisp five-pound notes stuffed into his hand with the last wages left the shell-shocked Elkins stammering his thanks. Willy had done what he could for him, writing directly to Whetstone explaining about him and his disability and asking if there was any chance of his being taken on by the new owners. Whetstone had replied that he was sure employment would be found for Elkins, hinting at a better and more remunerative position. Whetstone appeared to be a man who meant what he said, so Willy was satisfied, though he said nothing to Elkins about it in case the job did not materialize after all.

The estate car disappeared out of sight with Miss Ann still waving from the back seat. Slowly Elkins replaced his hat. If they were all like them life would be easier and better.

The men touched their caps and spat into their palms by way of time-honoured tradition. They did not really spit on the coin for luck and they did not have a coin in their hands either—they had two one-pound notes each. The furniture was all in and they were all in. The removal was complete.

The overflow of Willy's antique stock was out in the workshop and piled up in the garage, just leaving room for the brake. The silver, carefully packed by Willy himself, was up in the roof space, and the spare bedrooms were packed with goods not to be seen by unwanted dealers. Three things had been broken and then only by accident after arrival.

Ethel had the kettle on, and Ann was combing the local shops for something to eat for tea and supper. Willy crossed over to the other side of the road. His eyes scanned the ground-floor windows, then swung up to drink in the huge sign, each letter lovingly and carefully cut from the solid wood—a 'welcoming' present from old Newman the cabinet-maker, who was going to work for Willy every morning, six days of the week:

𝔚𝔦𝔩𝔩𝔦𝔞𝔪 𝔖𝔥𝔞𝔲𝔫
:: 𝔄𝔫𝔱𝔦𝔮𝔲𝔢𝔰 ::

Yes, and the antiques inside are going to be antiques, too, he told himself. None of your reproduction and fake stuff and no pretty-pretty, arty-arty muck either. Old Minden had a good reputation. It is up to me to follow on. From now on I'll deal hard but straight. No more 'tapping' and no more knockout money. I'm not going into the settlement again—they can keep it. I'm big enough to stop out of it. If the boys get nasty it will be a bit grim at first, but I'll outbid them for what I want. If I buy the right kind of stuff I'll hold most of Charlie's customers. Ann will have to sort *them* out. If only you could see me now, Dad, you'd be as proud as I am—William Shaun Esq.—mustn't forget the esquire—Connoisseur of Fine Art. Dammit, with a shop like this, I can perhaps afford to pay income tax!

He was pleased with his new world. Little did he know that the state was about to twist his tail hard—that almost at once the ratable value of the property and business was going to be reassessed—that instead of paying twenty-three shillings in the pound on a ratable value of one hundred and twenty pounds he was shortly to pay eighteen shillings in the pound on a reassessed ratable value of nine hundred and fifty pounds. His appeal was going to be dismissed and for once, cogitate how he might, there was going to be no way round the problem—no loophole. Of all this, however, he was blissfully unaware.

Ann came bounding along the street, parcels under her arms, breathless, with sparkling eyes.

'Here are all the local papers, Dad. Last week's as well as this. I thought you might like to know what is going on regarding the auction sales.'

She passed on, radiant, into the shop with her parcels.

In the office behind a fine antique showroom in London a gentleman turned over a page near the back cover of a trade magazine. He ran his eye over the advertisements.

H'm! Somebody by the name of Shaun has taken over Charlie Minden's business. Shaun?—never heard of him. Ought to nose down there and look him over before anyone else gets the same idea—he may have some decent goods.